THE
CLOCK
WE
LIVE
ON

THE
CLOCK
WE

by ISAAC ASIMOV PhD

LIVE
ON

REVISED EDITION

illustrated with diagrams by John Bradford

ABELARD-SCHUMAN *London   New York   Toronto*

SCIENCE BOOKS BY ISAAC ASIMOV

Building Blocks of the Universe, Revised Edition
    (winner of Edison Foundation Award)
The Chemicals of Life
The Clock We Live On, Revised Edition
The Double Planet
Inside the Atom, Revised Edition
The Kingdom of the Sun, Revised Edition
The Living River
Only a Trillion
Races and People
(with William C. Boyd)
The Wellsprings of Life
The World of Carbon
The World of Nitrogen

Library of Congress Catalogue
Card Number 65-12072

LONDON	NEW YORK	TORONTO
Abelard-Schuman	Abelard-Schuman	Abelard-Schuman
Limited	Limited	Canada Limited
8 King St. WC2	6 West 57th St.	896 Queen St. W.

Printed in the United States of America

TO DAVID on whose
seventh birthday
this book was
completed

CONTENTS

CONTENTS

ILLUSTRATIONS

9

CHAPTER 1

Following the Sun

One of the first things a youngster learns, once he starts school, is how to "tell time." Actually, this means he must learn to read the face of a clock.

Telling time is a useful accomplishment, even for a child. It is the way of checking whether lunch-time is near (or bed-time, perhaps), and it will tell you if a favorite television program is about to start.

The older we grow, the more we seem to live by the clock. Everything is run by the clock—jobs, mail deliveries, store-closings, movie-shows.

Another way of noting the passing of time is to look at the calendar. In that way, we find out when vacations will start and holidays come; or when bills are due; or when it is time to start thinking of buying a birthday present or shopping for Christmas.

The clock and the calendar are taken so much for granted, in fact, that few of us stop to wonder how mankind ever learned to tell time in the first place. It seems easy now, and every child is expected to understand it. Yet it took mankind thousands of years to puzzle out a system and in some ways it isn't worked out perfectly even yet.

This book is concerned with the troubles and triumphs of "telling time."

11

THE CLOCK WE LIVE ON

Which Moves ?

We live on the surface of a large ball of matter we call the Earth, which is constantly spinning. This spinning motion is referred to as the Earth's *rotation* (from a Latin word meaning "to turn"). The rotation proceeds at a steady rate year after year after year.

Imagine yourself out in space, watching a mark on the surface of the spinning Earth. As the mark passes directly before your eye, you set a clock in motion. Then you wait.

The mark moves off, carried by the Earth's rotation to the edge of the globe, then behind it, where you can see it no longer. Invisibly, it travels about the other side and eventually appears again at the other edge. Now it approaches you again and, as it passes directly before your eyes, you stop the clock.

If you check the clock now, you will find that the mark has moved completely about the Earth in 24 hours. If you repeated the experiment over and over again, you would find the same answer every time.

In other words, the Earth's *period of rotation* is 24 hours.

Of course, it is only in the last few hundred years that (except for a rare individual now and then, who guessed or reasoned out the truth) human beings have realised the Earth is spinning. To us on the Earth's surface, there is no sensation of motion at all. Everything seems perfectly stationary.

Instead, it is the sky and all the objects in it (the sun, the moon, the planets and stars) that seem to be moving. A star that happens to be overhead at a certain moment, drifts slowly and steadily westward, reaches the horizon and disappears. After a period of time, it appears again on the eastern horizon and climbs upward. When it is overhead again, 24 hours have passed.

This daily rotation of the sky and the "heavenly bodies" in it, from east to west is an illusion; Actually our planet and we are moving from west to east. It is the same sort of illusion we have when we are sitting in a train next to another train and begin to move smoothly forward. It often appears to us that we are stationary; that it is the other train that is moving backward.

What convinces us that we are wrong might be the sensation of the vibration or unsteadiness of our own train as it moves. Or else we look out of the other window and see that the station and the trees also seem to be moving backward. We know they can't move, so we are convinced we are moving.

Earth's motion, however, is perfectly smooth and can't be felt. Nor is there any "station" to look at and convince us that it is we who are moving and not the sky. At least, no "station" that could be seen by primitive man.

And so, for many thousands of years, even after man was quite civilized and not at all primitive, it was taken for granted that it was the sky and not the Earth that moved.

In some ways, this mistake was a bad one. It held back the science of astronomy. In other ways, it made no difference. For instance, in measuring time, we might as well assume the sky moves.

It is the apparent motion of the heavenly bodies, in fact, resulting from the actual motion of the Earth, that gave mankind its first notion of time. For that reason, we can think of ourselves as living on a giant clock; the first clock mankind ever had and still the most important.

Letting the Sun do the Work

There are thousands of heavenly bodies in the sky that take part in this motion from horizon to horizon and back. Of

13

these, the most important, by far, is the sun. No man, however primitive, could help but notice the sun.

When the sun is above the horizon, the world is flooded with light and warmth. A man can see to hunt for food and to protect himself while doing so. He can go about the business of life.

When the sun is below the horizon, darkness comes and with it, cold. Nightprowling beasts make life more dangerous. Even after the discovery of fire eased the worst perils of darkness, there was still little to do at such a time but to find a secure place to sleep.

This alteration of *day* and *night* must have been observed from the beginning and itself offers a way of keeping time. A journey might take so many days and nights. An event might have taken place so many days ago or may be expected to take place so many days in the future.

However, the period from sunrise to sunset, or from sunset to sunrise, is a long time. Telling someone, "Meet me at the corner of Fifth and Main tomorrow," isn't very useful. Your friend is bound to say, "What time tomorrow?"

The first method of breaking up the day into smaller portions must have involved the general position of the sun. Was it high in the sky or low in the sky? Was it rising or setting? To this day we still use general names for various parts of the day that date back to this way of looking at things. We talk of *dawn, morning, midday,* or *evening.* Duels may be fought at *sunrise* and sweethearts may meet at *sunset.*

But if we're going to use the position of the sun to guide us in breaking up the day, why not do the job thoroughly? The sun, after all, casts a shadow. When the sun is high in the sky, the shadow is short; when it is low in the sky,

14

the shadow is long. Furthermore, during the first half of the day, when the sun is in the east, the shadow points to the west. In the second half of the day, when the sun is in the west, the shadow points to the east. This notion of using a moving shadow to tell time originated in some forgotten period of the past in either Egypt or Babylonia. Perhaps it originated in both countries independently.

Any instrument which enables us to tell time by shadows is called a *sundial*. The word "dial" comes from a Latin word meaning "day," so a "sundial" is something that tells the time of day by means of the sun.

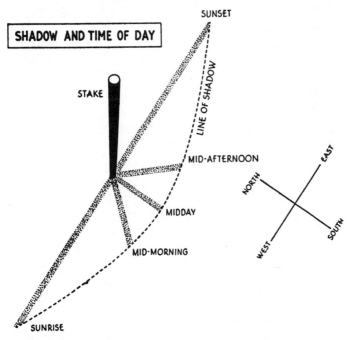

The simplest sundial need be nothing more than a wooden stake pounded vertically into the ground. Suppose you follow the shadow of the stake from sunrise to sunset, making a mark at the point where the shadow ends.

When those marks were connected, they would form a curved line, lying to one side of the stake. If the sun were directly overhead in the middle of the day, the shadow of the stake would disappear at that moment. And in that case, the line of the shadow would pass through the stake and be perfectly straight.

There are places on earth where the sun is, sometimes, directly overhead at midday, but this never happens in northern Egypt or in Babylonia. (Or, for that matter, in Europe or in the United States.) In those places at midday, the sun is always a little to the south of overhead, so that the shadow is always cast to the north then. The shadow is shorter at midday than at any other time, but it does not disappear.

This is not a serious matter. For one thing, instead of using a simple stake, you could use one that is nailed into a horizontal bar at the bottom, with a shorter horizontal bar nailed crosswise on top. Then, even though the path of the shadow curved, part of the shadow of the cross-bar on top would always fall on the horizontal bar below.

Such a device used to tell time by the sun was called a *gnomon* by the Greeks. In Greek, this means "one who knows," since a man using a sundial knows the time of day by observing the shadow on the gnomon. (Sundials were first introduced into Greece, probably from Babylonia, in about 575 B.C.), but the Egyptians may have been using forms of sundials a thousand years before that.

In any case, whether you follow the shadow of the stake along a curve or a straight line, that line can be divided into sections, and the sections can be numbered. Such sections are called *hours*, from a Greek word meaning "time of day."

The number of hours into which the line of the moving shadow was divided was 12. This dates back to the Babylonians, who had a liking for the number 12. Twelve can be divided evenly by 2, 3, 4 or 6 and is therefore a convenient number to use. In ancient times, mathematical

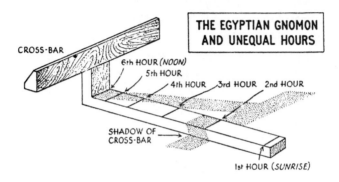

THE EGYPTIAN GNOMON AND UNEQUAL HOURS

CROSS-BAR

6th HOUR *(NOON)*
5th HOUR
4th HOUR   3rd HOUR   2nd HOUR

SHADOW OF CROSS-BAR

1st HOUR *(SUNRISE)*

techniques for handling fractions were not well worked out. Therefore a number that could be divided in several different ways without producing fractions was a desirable one.

Our own modern tendency is to divide measurements into 10 parts. Still, many common measurements retain the use of division by 12 from primitive times. Thus, there are 12 inches in a foot, 12 ounces in a Troy pound, 12 pence in a shilling, 12 dozen in a gross, and 12 of anything in a dozen.

When sundials first came into use, the hours were numbered starting at sunrise, naturally. Midday came at the end of the sixth hour and sunset at the end of the twelfth. Thus, the Biblical phrase, "the eleventh hour" does not mean the hour before midnight as most people seem to think. It means the time when only one more hour of sunlight is left.

The ninth hour, called "nona" in Latin, was the middle of the second half of the day, ending just half-way between midday and sunset. Somehow, this middle of the second half of the day became confused with the middle of the day itself. In English, we speak of midday as *noon*, the first half of the day as *forenoon* (a contraction of "before noon") and the second half of the day as *afternoon*.

The Catholic church still numbers the hours from the sunrise in connection with certain prayers that must be said by priests. These *canonical hours* include *prime* ("one"), which is at 6 in the morning. Then there is *tierce* ("three"), at 9 in the morning; *sext* ("six") at 12 noon, and *none* ("nine"), at 3 in the afternoon.

Shortcomings of the Sun

There are some difficulties concerning the sundial. For instance, if a shadow is allowed to fall on a flat surface, it moves quite rapidly in the morning but slows as it approaches midday. After midday it starts speeding up and near sunset it is moving quite rapidly again.

That means that if you divide the line of shadow into equal parts, the morning and evening hours will pass quickly, while the midday hours will pass slowly. Rather than have that happen, the ancient Egyptians divided the segments unequally, making rather long segments at both ends of the line and short segments in the middle. In this way, the hours are made of equal duration.

Another way out is not to have the shadow fall on a flat surface. The Babylonians, for instance, in the third century, B.C., invented a type of sundial in which the *style* (the part of the sundial that casts the shadow) was set within a kind of bowl. This was so designed that the line

18

FOLLOWING THE SUN

of shadow followed a path around the edge of the bowl, moving at a steady rate. If that path were divided into equal segments, you got equal hours.

(Many different types of sundials have been designed in the past three thousand years or so, and it is the oldest scientific instrument still in use in its original form. Some are ornamental enough to be placed in the gardens and on lawns even today, just for their fine appearance. The most familiar type, perhaps, is one in which the style is slanted toward the north. The dial is in the form of a flat circle, around the rim of which the shadow will fall. The Romans even invented a small sundial that could be carried about like a modern watch, and in 290 B.C. they erected a public sundial so that anyone passing by could tell the time.)

Another problem is that the path followed by the shadow is not the same day after day. During the summer and fall, the path shifts slightly northward each day, and then during the winter and spring, it shifts slightly southward again. This isn't too bad because the shadow never strays outside certain limits. If the marked line on the sundial is correctly drawn and the style correctly designed, some part of the shadow will always cross the line in such a way as to give the hour.

Unfortunately, though, as the shadow shifts northward, the sun makes the trip from one horizon to the other more rapidly. In New York City, for instance, when the shadow is at the northern limit, the day is only 3/5 as long as it is when the shadow is at the southern limit.

Yet on every day the sun travels from horizon to horizon and the shadow must move from end to end of the sundial. When the day is shorter, the shadow must travel more quickly to complete its journey. As measured by the

19

sundial then, the hours hurry past on the short days of the year and lag on the long days.

In the early days of time-keeping, this was endured without much fuss. Hours were long and short at different times, just as days were long and short. No one minded much.

(You may wonder at this point, incidentally, why there should be long days and short days if the Earth rotates at a steady rate. This will be discussed later in the book.)

Still another shortcoming of the sundial was that it only worked when the sun was in the sky. Clouds interfered. And, of course, night interfered. To most people this didn't matter. Night was a time for sleeping, not for wondering what hour it might be.

However, on shipboard and in armies on campaign, some men always had to be awake and on watch for danger throughout the night. For them, time by night was important since usually a number of men shared the work, one after the other, and no man wanted to stay on duty longer than his fair share of the night.

At first, probably, the changing position of certain prominent stars was used to divide the night into twelve hours, in imitation of the day. Then each man who was assigned night duty would watch for so many hours. The Hebrews divided the night into three *watches* of four hours each. The Greeks and Romans divided it into four watches of three hours each. Soldiers and sailors might then speak of events taking place in the first watch of the night, or in the second. We still have the poetic phrase, "the silent watches of the night" to commemorate the old system.

Improving on the Sun

But what about telling time indoors, where there is no question of either sun or stars at any time? What is needed is something which, indoors, would have regular motion, as regular or almost as regular as those of the heavenly bodies.

One of the oldest solutions to this problem was the use of a burning candle. A large candle burned downward at a fairly steady rate. If such a candle were allowed to burn while a sundial was being watched, then, at the end of each hour, what was left of it could be matched against similar unburnt candles. Marks could be made on those other candles to show the points to which they ought to burn after one hour, after two hours and so on. Oil lamps could also be used for the purpose. The oil supply in a transparent cylinder gradually drops as the lamp burns, and the cylinder need merely be marked off for hours.

Such candles could then replace the sundial altogether on cloudy days. They could be used indoors. They could be started at any time and put out when not needed. They were more than mere substitutes for the sundial; in some ways, they were improvements.

A still better device was the *hour-glass*, invented about 250 B.C. and familiar to all of us. Sand pours from the upper half of the hour-glass into the lower through a narrow constriction. It pours slowly and by putting the right amount of pure, dry sand in it, one could make the pouring last for exactly one hour, for instance. By then turning it upside-down one could start it going on the next hour.

The use of half-hour hour-glasses on board some ancient vessel may be the origin of the traditional way of signalling the passing of time on shipboard. Starting at midnight, the passing of each half-hour (when it was time to turn the hour-glass) was marked by a bell.

Half an hour after midnight was "one bell." One hour after was "two bells" and so on. Finally, four hours after midnight, or "eight bells," was the end of a watch, so a new series of bells began. Four and a half hours after midnight was "one bell" again.

In this way, there are six series of bell soundings, from one to eight, during a day and night. This may seem confusing, but a sailor would know which watch it was from the position of the sun or stars. His main interest would be to know how much of the watch was over, and the bells would tell him that.

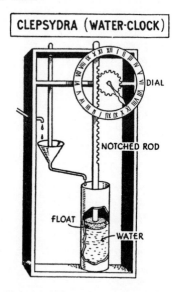

CLEPSYDRA (WATER-CLOCK)

DIAL

NOTCHED ROD

FLOAT

WATER

A similar idea was the *water-clock* or *clepsydra*, which was introduced into the Graeco-Roman world (probably from Egypt where it had been used at least as long as 1500 B.C.) about 150 B.C. In the clepsydra, water was allowed to drip through a narrow opening into a container where it collected. The water dripped through at a steady rate, so that the container filled up at a steady rate. Markings on the container (like those on the burning candle) would tell the passage of hours by the rise in the water level.

Elaborate clepsydras included a float on the water which rose as the water-level in the container rose. This float was attached to a notched rod which turned a gear as it pushed upward. A pointer was attached to the gear by one end so that as the water-level rose, the pointer turned in a circle. Behind the pointer was a dial marked off with even sections numbered from one to twelve. (This begins to look something like our modern clocks.)

Clepsydras were the most advanced time-telling devices in the ancient world. In 800 A.D., the Arabian caliph, Harun al-Rashid (of Arabian Nights fame) sent a mechanical clock to Charlemagne. It was too much for the Europeans to duplicate, however. It was not until 1300 A.D. that Europeans began to build mechanical clocks, somewhere in northern Italy or southern Germany. The gears controlling the movement of the pointer were now powered by slowly descending weights rather than slowly rising water. (No splashing or worries about running dry.) Such clocks were set in the towers of cathedrals for all the town to see. By 1472, a German astronomer called Regiomantanus (his real name was Johann Müller) was using weight-driven clocks in his observatory.

Another advance was made about 1550 when coiled springs instead of weights were used to drive the gears. This meant that clocks could be made more compact. They were no longer confined to church steeples but could be brought into the home.

The Turning Point
None of these mechanical devices, run by rising water

or falling weights, were very accurate. You were lucky if you could tell the time to the nearest hour. The very best mechanical clocks could not keep time to better than 5 minutes a day, as late as 1650. (Perhaps, prior to modern times, this was good enough. There were no railway trains keeping schedules to the minute, or radio and television shows beginning on the second.)

To make devices more accurate, one had to find something that could be relied upon to move even more steadily and faithfully than dripping water or falling weights.

The turning point came in 1581. In that year, a seventeen-year-old Italian boy named Galileo Galilei watched a swinging chandelier in the Cathedral of Pisa (instead of listening to services). He noticed that whether the draft swung the chandelier in a wide arc or in a narrow one, it seemed to take the same time moving from end to end. He checked this by timing it against the throbbing of his pulse.

A *pendulum* (that is, a weight suspended from a rod or string, from a Latin word meaning "swinging") does indeed swing from side to side in a nearly fixed time. The time of swing depends upon the length of the pendulum. The length can be adjusted, for instance, so that the pendulum completes its swing in exactly one second. (Such a pendulum the French mathematician, Marin Mersenne, discovered in 1644, must be about 39.1 inches long.)

About 1657, the Dutch astronomer, Christiaan Huyghens, invented a clock in which falling weights kept a pendulum going and the regular motion of the pendulum (rather than of the weights themselves) ran the "clockwork." Such "grandfathers' clocks" were much more reliable than anything that went before and, in fact, are still in use today. Even the first pendulum clock didn't gain or lose more than 10 seconds a day. By 1730 that had been cut down to 1 second, by 1830 to 1/10 second, by 1885 to 1/100 second, and by 1925 to 1/5,000 second.

(The word "clock" is a reminder of the time when churches were in charge of time-keeping. The passage of time was indicated by the ringing of church bells, as on shipboard, except that there was one bell for each hour, not half-hour, from one to twelve. The word "clock" originally meant "bell," for in French, the word for "bell" is "cloche."

A pendulum clock, however, cannot be used on shipboard where the motion of the ship would throw off the pendulum. Yet clocks were desperately needed on ships.

Fortunately, objects smaller than pendulums will also move very regularly. A fine spring of tempered steel (a *hair-spring* invented by Huyghens in 1675) can be made to tighten and loosen in a regular rhythm. If such a spring is kept in motion by a slowly unwinding *main-spring,* it can be made to control the clockwork, and a small clock can be manufactured (though small clocks without hair-springs, and therefore very poor timekeepers, were manufactured as early as 1510.) Such clocks, small enough to fit in a pocket, can withstand the rocking of a ship, and must have been of particular use to people standing watch on ship. They are called *watches* to this day.

After World War I, it became fashionable to place straps on watches and wear them on the wrist. Pocket watches went out of fashion and *wrist-watches* were all the thing. I am wearing a wrist-watch right now, as I do at all times. I would feel undressed without it.

25

Equalizing the Hour

The various time-keeping devices, from burning candles onward, worked an important change in the nature of the hour as a time interval. As I have already said, the shadow of a sun-dial moves at different speeds on different days so that hours are longer or shorter with the season of the year. (Hours that are allowed to vary in length with the season are called *temporal hours.*) Candles, however, burn at nearly the same rate every day of the year (a little faster on warm days perhaps). Sand, water weights, pendulums and springs all likewise move at the same rate every day of the year.

The notion therefore arose of *equal hours* from day to day, regardless of the sun, and this notion took over. The coming of the mechanical clock was the final touch, though even as late as 1600 some attempt was made to adjust clocks to record unequal hours. The length of the hour stopped changing with the season. This means there are times during the year when daylight lasts less than twelve hours and times when it endures more. The same is true of night. But what about day plus night?

Even primitive man must have noticed that when days were short, nights were long, and vice versa. The use of time-telling devices showed the relationship to be quite an exact one. If the day grew shorter, the night grew just enough longer to make up for it and vice versa. The day and night together never changed in length and could be broken up into 24 unchanging hours throughout. So the 24-hour period became more important than either day or night.

Yet although the notion of the 24-hour time period has been established for at least two thousand years, old habits die hard. The 24-hour period is still so "new-fangled" that it has never been given a name. In English, we call it a "day" but that is a borrowed name from the period of light. If we say "day," do we mean the time from sunrise to sunset or the time from sunrise to the next sunrise? For instance, we speak of June 21 as the "longest day of the year." It is, of course, no longer than any other day, being 24 hours long like all the rest. But here we are referring to the daylight hours only, the older and original "day." This older meaning is sometimes referred to as *natural day* to distinguish it from the newer 24-hour meaning.

Furthermore, our clocks are still divided into 12 hours, not 24. If we say "three o'clock" ("o'clock" is a contraction, by the way, for the phrase "of the clock"), we cannot know for certain whether this refers to a time of daylight or of night.

The armed forces of the United States have tried to eliminate this uncertainty by counting the hours through to 24 so that "three o'clock" is "three at night" and "fifteen o'clock" is "three in the afternoon." The civilian population, however, is still not adopting this "new-fangled" attitude, which is only two thousand years old.

Dividing the Hour

Once the notion of equal hours was established, moreover, it was natural to think of dividing the hours into smaller units for convenience sake, all the smaller units also being equal. Once pendulum clocks came into use, time-keeping became accurate enough to make such division possible.

By a proper adjustment of gears, a new pointer could be attached to the dial that would turn twelve times as fast as the old pointer. It would make a complete circuit of the dial in the time the old pointer moved one hour. Each time this new pointer passed an hour marking, 1/12 of an hour would have passed.

If the space between the hour marks were divided into five equal divisions, then each time the new pointer passed one of those small divisions 1/60 of an hour would have passed. These small intervals of 1/60 of an hour are called minutes (from a Latin word meaning "small").

Even earlier, hours must have been divided roughly into halves and quarters and we still speak of "half past six" and "a quarter to seven." Once minutes were established, though, we could speak of "five past six" or "thirteen to seven." The most logical method of indicating time is simply to say 6:05 or 6:47 for those last two phrases. The symbol 6:00 would represent 6 o'clock exactly. (The armed forces use symbols such as 1522 for twenty-two minutes after three in the afternoon, even leaving out the colon. They say 0322 for twenty-two minutes after three at night.)

Eventually, still another pointer could be added which would make a complete circuit of the dial in a minute. Every time it passed one of the 60 small divisions on the dial, 1/60 of a minute would have passed. This new, still smaller unit of time is called a *second* (because it is the second division of the hour, the division of a previous division).

The three pointers, or *hands* of a modern clock are thus termed the *hour hand*, the *minute hand*, and the *second hand*. The hour hand is the "little hand" because it need only point in the direction of the hour marking. The minute hand is the "big hand" because it must reach all the way to the small markings so that we can read the exact minute. The second hand is on a separate smaller dial, or, if not, is often colored red so that even a rapid glance at the clock will cause no confusion.

FOLLOWING THE SUN

You may wonder if there's any reason why the division of the hour should be by sixties. Why should there be 60 seconds to the minute and 60 minutes to the hour? Why not 10? or 100?

The use of 60 dates back to the Babylonians, who used it a great deal because of the fact that it could be divided evenly in a number of ways. I have already mentioned their use of 12, which can be divided evenly by 2, 3, 4, and 6. Twelve cannot, however, be divided by 5. The lowest number which can be divided by 2, 3, 4, 6, and by 5 in addition, is 60. (To top it off, 60 can also be divided by 10, 12, 15, 20, and 30.)

This *sexagesimal system* (from a Latin word meaning "sixty") breaks down for units of time less than a second. Few people even in our own time-conscious days are interested in time-intervals of less than a second, unless they are clocking horse-races. Scientists, however, are forced to consider tiny fractions of a second at times.

Scientists, of course, are used to working with the metric system, in which all units are divided and subdivided by tens. They divide up the second in this way and call a thousandth of a second a *millisecond*, and a millionth of a second a *microsecond*. (The prefixes "milli-" and "micro-" are used in the metric system to signify a thousandth and a millionth, respectively, of any unit.)

CHAPTER 2

Slicing up Heaven and Earth

Beginning in the Middle

Once the 24-hour day came into use, there arose the question of when to start and end the day. As long as day and night were timed separately, there was no question. The day started at sunrise and the night started at sunset. The first tendency, naturally, was to continue this and to start the 24-hour day at either sunrise or sunset.

The Egyptians started the day-night combination at sunrise and the Hebrews at sunset. Even today, Jewish holidays such as Rosh Hashonah (New Year) and Yom Kippur (Day of Atonement) start at sunset and end at sunset. The period immediately following the coming of the sunset that begins the holiday is called "Erev Rosh Hashonah" or "Erev Yom Kippur." The word "erev" means "evening," so that "Erev Yom Kippur," for instance, means "the evening of Yom Kippur."

This habit carries over into Christian holidays. When we speak of "Christmas Eve" and "New Year's Eve," we don't mean the evenings of Christmas and New Year (December 25 and January 1) but the evenings before Christmas and New Year (December 24 and December 31).

Actually, though, beginning the day at either sunrise or sunset has certain disadvantages. For one thing neither sunrise nor sunset occurs in the same part of the day from season to season. Sunrise in New York City occurs much later at the beginning of winter than at the beginning of summer. When we wake up in December it is still dark. It is dark again before we have had time to eat dinner. When we wake in June, the sun has been in the sky for hours and it remains in the sky long after dinner.

As the sun rises earlier and earlier and sets later and later all through the winter and spring, the time from sunrise to sunrise or from sunset to sunset is a bit more than 24 hours. During summer and fall, the situation is reversed, and the time from sunrise to sunrise or from sunset to sunset is less than 24 hours.

All these changes are not too important in an agricultural society where work must follow the sun anyway. As the more artificial town life grew important, however, something more constant was needed.

The "something more constant" was the time at which the sun was directly overhead. According to clepsydrae, for instance, it was always just about 24 hours between times when the sun was overhead, regardless of the season of the year. If the sun rose earlier, it set correspondingly later (or vice versa) and reached the middle of its journey at about the same time.

Consequently, it seemed more practical to start counting from midday and by Roman times this was done. One hour after midday was 1 o'clock, two hours after was 2 o'clock and so on. By the time 12 o'clock rolled around it was midnight. The series then started again. An hour after midnight was 1 o'clock once more and this continued until at midday it was 12 o'clock again.

(Two 12 hour intervals per day hung on out of habit, even though they no longer had anything to do with day and night. As we shall see over and over again in this book, force of habit is nowhere stronger than in connection with the way we tell time.)

The Latin word for "midday" is "meridianus." It is common, then, to speak of the time at midday as "12 meridian" which is abbreviated 12 M. The hours numbered 1 to 12 following midday are then "post meridian" (Latin for "after midday" or, as we commonly say, "afternoon"). This is abbreviated as P.M. The hours numbered 1 to 12 preceding midday are correspondingly "ante meridian" (Latin for "before midday" or "forenoon"). This is abbreviated A.M.

In this way we can distinguish the daylight 3 o'clock and the night-time 3 o'clock. The former is 3 P.M. and the latter 3 A.M.

The 24-hour day might start either at 12 M. (noon) or 12 P.M. (midnight). Starting it at noon, as the ancient Egyptians did, would cut the business day in half. Business transacted in the A.M. hours would be dated, for instance, March 5, while business transacted in the P.M. hours would be dated March 6. Opportunities for confusion would be endless.

It seems logical, then, to start the day at midnight when everyone (or nearly everyone) is safely asleep and doesn't mind. You wake to a new day and keep that new day till bedtime.

Astronomers, who work through the night (and sleep through the day, I guess) found it convenient, for the same reason, to start the day at noon. This so-called *astronomical time* is half a day behind ordinary time. Thus 3 A.M. on June 5 in ordinary time would be 15 o'clock on June 5 in astronomical time. After 1925,

however, astronomers switched to the midnight beginning and are now in step with the rest of the world.

The Divisions of Heaven

It now becomes important in time-keeping to consider the
moment at which the sun is directly overhead (or at the
zenith). The Babylonians had tried to pinpoint the position
of heavenly bodies in the sky, and to help themselves do
so they divided the heavens by a series of imaginary lines
running due north and south. The entire vault of the
heavens was divided by exactly 360 such lines, equally
spaced. (Why 360? I'll explain that later in the book.)

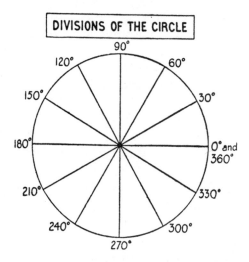

The lines that divided the sky seemed to be a series of
steps down which you could go in passing from zenith to
horizon. These 360 divisions of the sky are called *degrees*
from a Latin word meaning "down steps." Ever since

Babylonian times, it has been customary to divide all circles and spheres into 360 degrees.

Other types of divisions may also be called degrees, as, for instance, the degrees of temperature on a thermometer. The degrees marking off a circle or sphere are distinguished from other types of degrees by being called *degrees of arc*. (An "arc" is a portion of the curve of a circle.)

The distance half-way around any circle or sphere, as, for instance, from horizon to horizon along the great sphere of the sky, is half of 360, or 180 degrees. The distance from horizon to zenith is half of 180, or 90 degrees.

Each degree is divided into 60 *minutes of arc* (the "of arc" distinguishes it from minutes of time) and each minute is divided into 60 *seconds of arc*. Here again, the Babylonian use of the sexagesimal system shows itself.

At first the sun was considered to be at zenith (and the time was noon) when the shadow on the sundial was at its shortest. This was not a very accurate way of deciding. In 1731, an Englishman named John Hadley invented a device to do the job better. It is now called a *sextant* and consists of a curved arc, making up a sixth of a circle (the word "sextant" comes from a Latin word meaning "sixth") and marked off into 120 divisions, each division being half a degree.

The sextant is equipped with two mirrors, one of which is used to sight the horizon. (This works best at sea where there are no hills, trees or houses to obscure the horizon.) The second mirror is used to sight the sun. The result is that the angle between the two mirrors, when both are properly lined up, is just half the amount by which the sun is raised above the horizon. (Why half? That follows from certain optical laws of light reflection which I can't go into here.)

The angle between the mirrors can be determined from

two pointers attached to the mirrors, which move against the markings on the arm. The markings are in half-degrees, so they give the height of the sun in full degrees, since the angle between the mirrors must be doubled.

When the sun is 90 degrees above the horizon, as measured by the sextant, it is midday.

The imaginary north-south line that passes through the zenith of the sky is 90 degrees from the horizon and it is what must be straddled by the sun at midday. This line is therefore the *meridian*. By comparing a clock with the results of a sextant determination one can fix the time when the sun "crosses the meridian." Then the clock can be adjusted if it is too fast or too slow.

Modern time-pieces, however, have become so accurate that we have taken to adjusting the sun instead. For reasons I'll mention later in the book, the time between successive crossings of the meridian is not exactly 24 hours after all. The sun may lag or gain as much as 15 minutes of time and cross the meridian, in other words, as early as 11:45 A.M. or as late as 12:15 P.M.

Does this mean that the Earth's spin is wobbly?

To decide that, we've got to remember that the sun is not the only object that rises, crosses the meridian and sets. Other heavenly bodies do that.

Suppose that, instead of the sun, you observe a particular star each night and note the time at which it crosses the meridian. You will find that in that case there is an equal interval between successive crossings. The star, unlike the sun, moves steadily. The star is never as much as a second early or a second late and this is true no matter which star we observe.

The time between one crossing of the meridian by a star and the next is called the *sidereal day* (from the Latin

35

word "sidus" meaning "star"). From the fact that the sidereal day is quite steady, we can see that the Earth is rotating evenly. The erratic behavior of the sun is not due to any unevenness in the Earth's spin but to other motions of the Earth which I have yet to talk about.

The time between one crossing of the meridian by the sun and the next is the *solar day* (from the Latin "sol" meaning "sun"). Since the solar day varies a bit with the slight earliness and lateness of the sun from day to day, it is customary to average the length of the solar day over an entire year. This is called the *mean solar day* (the word "mean" meaning "average" when used in this sense), or the *civil day*.

The *mean sun* would therefore be an imaginary sun at the place where the real sun would be if it went around the Earth as evenly as a star. Noon comes when the mean sun, not the real sun, crosses the meridian.

Time based on the mean sun is called *mean time*. Time based on the real sun is *apparent time*. Thus, each day, there is a *mean noon* when the mean sun crosses the meridian and an *apparent noon* when the real sun does. These two noons may be as much as fifteen minutes apart, but four times a year they coincide. The difference between the mean and apparent noon as this varies from day to day is called the *equation of time*.

You might expect, now, that the mean solar day, with all the unevennesses of the sun's motion averaged out, would be just as long as the sidereal day, but it is not. The mean solar day is defined as exactly 24 hours long to the split-second. The sidereal day, as measured by today's accurate time-pieces, is about 4 minutes shorter. It is, to be exact, 23 hours 56 minutes 4·09 seconds long.

I will come back to this difference between the sidereal

36

day and the mean solar day later in the book, because it is important.

The Divisions of Earth

Many of the ancient Greek thinkers had decided the Earth was round. Some of the maps of the known world which they drew, were marked off by north-south lines like those drawn in the heavens by the Babylonians.

To a man in Athens, the north-south line in the sky that passed through the zenith was directly over a north-south line on the surface of the Earth that passed through Athens, or, more exactly, through the place on which he was standing. To a man in Rome, it was the line through Rome, through himself, that corresponded to the line through the zenith. All the north-south lines on Earth are exactly under the meridian for people living on that particular line. For that reason, all the north-south lines drawn on maps of the Earth, all without exception, are called *meridians* to this day.

The ancients were content to talk of the "meridian of Athens," the "meridian of Rome" and so on. Travelers, however, especially those who went by sea, out of sight of ordinary landmarks, needed something more systematic than that.

It was natural, then, to divide up the globe of the Earth into 360 meridians, each representing one degree (following the Babylonian fashion). Each degree could then be divided into 60 minutes and each minute into 60 seconds.

If you'll look at a globe, you will see various meridians drawn north and south, converging and meeting at the North Pole and the South Pole. Not every degree is drawn; it would be too messy if they were. Usually, they are drawn at intervals of ten degrees. Notice that they seem to slice up the Earth into portions resembling segments of a tangerine.

A question arises as to exactly where to draw the meridians. They can be drawn anywhere, of course. A Greek geographer might begin by drawing a meridian through Athens and then mark off other meridians to the east and west. A Roman geographer might start with the meridian of Rome. An American geographer might start with the meridian of Times Square in New York.

This might be endurable if people concerned themselves only with small areas about their own chief cities. The

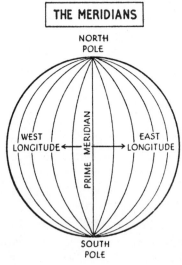

THE MERIDIANS

NORTH POLE

WEST LONGITUDE ← PRIME MERIDIAN → EAST LONGITUDE

SOUTH POLE

situation would be unbearable at sea, though, when ships of many nations are trying to keep track of their exact location. If one ship is using an Italian system based on Rome and another an American system based on New York, there would be endless confusion. One ship reporting its position to another, expecting rescue, might find that its rescuing ship had to delay while it figured out the ship's position in its own system.

No. By the time ocean travel had become commonplace, there had to be one system accepted by all the world. It was inevitable.

Such a system was agreed upon at the Washington Meridian Conference held in 1884. At the time Great Britain was the most powerful nation in the world and had the largest navy and merchant marine. It was, of all the nations, most concerned with sea-travel, and so its standard was adopted. The British counted their meridians from their astronomical observatory in Greenwich (a district of London) and the Greenwich meridian is therefore called the *Prime Meridian* ("prime" coming from a Latin word meaning "first"). The Greenwich Observatory has since moved to Hurstmonceaux on the English Channel, but the Prime Meridian has stayed put.

The meridians measure the east-west position of points on the Earth's surface. This east-west position is called *longitude*, because the meridians, which are drawn north-south, cross the maps long-ways. (Maps are usually drawn with north on top and south on bottom.)

Thus the Prime Meridian marks 0 degrees Longitude. (The word "degrees" is symbolized by a small zero to the upper right of the number, so that you might write the Prime Meridian as 0° Longitude.)

One can then mark off the degrees west all around the world, or east all around the world, counting them off to 360. Instead, it has become conventional to count them off in both directions at once. The meridians west of London (toward America) mark off *West Longitude*, those east of London (toward Asia) mark off *East Longitude*.

In this way, you can have a 75° West Longitude (which

runs through New York State) and a 75° East Longitude (which runs through India). All points on 75° West Longitude are 75 degrees west of Greenwich; all points on 75° East Longitude are 75 degrees east.

The two series of meridians are marked off east and west until they finally meet at the meridian exactly opposite to that of the Prime Meridian. This final meridian is 180° which, like 0° is neither East nor West Longitude.

The 180° meridian runs through the easternmost tip of Siberia and then down the length of the Pacific Ocean, touching hardly any land. This, as we shall soon see, is a good thing.

The usefulness of meridians, so far as time-keeping is concerned, is just this: the time of day varies from point to point on the Earth's surface and the meridians help us to keep the variations straight. To talk about that, though, let's start a new chapter.

CHAPTER 3

Time's Journey about the Earth

Local Time

If you visualize the Earth as a globe with the sun shining upon it, you can see that the time of day is not the same everywhere on Earth. For one thing, the half of Earth facing the sun is lit up and is enjoying day. The opposite half is in the shadow and is experiencing night. Where light and shadow meet, there is dawn and sunrise on one side of the Earth, twilight and sunset on the other.

Furthermore, if you concentrate on the sunlit portion of the Earth, you will see that the part of the Earth directly under the sun is marking noon (the passage of the sun across its meridian). Elsewhere, it is not noon.

Suppose, for instance, that the sun is directly above the Prime Meridian. It is therefore noon in London (and at every other point along the Prime Meridian).

But the Earth is spinning from west to east (or, if you prefer, the sun is moving from east to west; and it's easier to pretend the sun is moving for purposes of this chapter). Since the sun travels all around the 360° of Earth's longitude in 24 hours, it travels 360/24 or 15° in one hour. In one hour after London's noon, then, the sun will be overhead the 15° West Longitude line; in two hours it will be overhead the 30° West Longitude line and so on.

At noon in London then, it is still one hour before noon (or 11 A.M.) at 15° West Longitude and two hours before noon (or 10 A.M.) at 30° West Longitude.

It works similarly in the other direction. One hour before the sun had reached Prime Meridian, it had been over 15° East Longitude, and two hours before it had been over 30° East Longitude. This means that at noon in London, it is one hour after noon (1 P.M.) at 15° East Longitude and two hours after noon (2 P.M.) at 30° East Longitude.

In this way any point on Earth can fix its own particular time (*local time*) in comparison with the time at the Prime Meridian (*Greenwich time*). To do this, it is only necessary to know the longitude of the place on which you're standing. Subtract 1 hour from Greenwich time for every 15° (or 4 minutes for every 1°) that you are west of the Prime Meridian. Add 1 hour to Greenwich time for every 15° that you are east of the Prime Meridian. Your longitude tells you at once how many degrees, minutes and seconds you are east or west.

It works the other way, too. Suppose you have a clock that is adjusted to Greenwich time. Suppose you then determine when the sun is overhead ("local noon") by means of a sextant. You also need a table that will tell you how to add or subtract minutes on a particular day to change the real sun to the mean sun. By noting Greenwich time at your local noon, you can determine your longitude. For every 4 minutes that you are earlier than Greenwich time, you are 1° west of Greenwich; for every four minutes later, you are 1° east.

What is needed for this is an accurate clock which can be guaranteed to keep Greenwich time on board a rolling and pitching ship (since it is on ocean voyages that day-to-day knowledge of longitude is most important). Huyghens, after inventing the pendulum clock, tried some on board ship, but they wouldn't work on such an unsteady object.

The British government was especially interested in calculating longitude, for Britain was a seafaring nation. In 1675, Charles II had founded the Greenwich observatory in order to make astronomical observations that would help determine longitude.

Then, in 1714, the British government offered a reward of £20,000 for anyone devising a clock that would work on shipboard. (That's how important it is to know your position on ocean voyages.) In 1760, a Yorkshire carpenter named John Harrison (self-taught) devised a ship's *chronometer* (from Latin words meaning "time-measurer") that won the prize. To win it he had to build a more accurate clock than any known on land at the time and balance it on gimbals in such a way that it kept steady regardless of the ship's motion. (Nowadays, chronometers are no longer needed at all. Only a radio set is necessary so that standard time signals, which are more accurate than the reading of any ship's chronometer, can be picked up.)

Standard Time

Actually, it is inconvenient to allow each city to have its own local time. For instance, Boston is at 71° West Longitude and Philadelphia at 75° West Longitude. This means that at noon Greenwich time, it is 7:00 A.M. in Philadelphia and 7:16 A.M. in Boston.

In the days before modern transportation and communication these small differences might not matter. Each community might have its own local time in peace and quiet, especially if people didn't carry watches but depended on the local church steeples for the time.

TIME ZONES

PACIFIC STANDARD TIME 4 A.M

MOUNTAIN STANDARD TIME 5 A.M

CENTRAL STANDARD TIME 6 A.M

EASTERN STANDARD TIME 7 A.M

112½°

97½°

82½°

------- THEORETICAL BOUNDARIES OF TIME ZONES
——— LEGAL BOUNDARIES

NOTE: TIMES GIVEN FOR EACH ZONE ARE THOSE EXISTING WHEN IT IS NOON ON THE PRIME MERIDIAN

However, once trains started running, they couldn't put out time-tables that took into account the local time at every stop. Furthermore, imagine television programs starting on the hour (New York time) that had to be turned on four minutes before the hour in Philadelphia and twelve minutes after the hour in Boston!

This trouble was first felt by those nations which spread over considerable longitude and which were developing an advanced railroad network. This meant the United States and Canada. In 1878 a Canadian named Sandford Fleming suggested that the United States and Canada be divided into strips 15 degrees wide and that within the strips a single time of day be made legal. Charles Ferdinand Dowd of the United States also pioneered in this view.

This idea was finally adopted by the railroads, then by the nations, then by the world at large.

This is the way it works. At noon Greenwich time, let it be considered exactly noon (regardless of the actual position of the sun) everywhere between $7\frac{1}{2}°$ East Longitude and $7\frac{1}{2}°$ West Longitude. This is a 15° width altogether, and such a segment can be called a *zone*.

To the west of this "noon zone" is another 15° zone from $7\frac{1}{2}°$ West Longitude to $22\frac{1}{2}°$ West Longitude in which it is 11 A.M. everywhere. In the other direction, to the east of the "noon zone" there is one from $7\frac{1}{2}°$ East Longitude to $22\frac{1}{2}°$ East Longitude in which it is 1 P.M. everywhere.

In this way the Earth is divided up into 24 time-zones. The legal time within such a zone is called *zone time* or, more frequently, *standard time*.

The United States stretches across four such zones, centering about 75°, 90°, 105° and 120° West Longitude. The easternmost of these zones covers the eastern seaboard of the United States and within it there is *Eastern Standard Time*. To the west of this is a zone covering the Mississippi Valley, within which there is *Central Standard Time*. Next is the zone covering the Rocky Mountain area, within which is *Mountain Standard Time*. Farthest to the west is the zone covering the western seaboard, within which is *Pacific Standard Time*.

This means that at noon Greenwich, it is 7 A.M. in cities like Boston, New York, Philadelphia, Washington, Atlanta and Miami. It is 6 A.M. in cities like Minneapolis, Chicago, St. Louis, Houston and New Orleans. It is 5 A.M. in cities like Butte, Boise, Denver, Phoenix and Santa Fe. Finally, it is 4 A.M. in cities like Seattle, San Francisco, Los Angeles, and San Diego.

In traveling from one zone to the next, you must allow for a sudden jump of one hour. After you arrive in Chicago from New York, for instance, you must turn your watch one hour back. When you return to New York, you must push it one hour forward again. In making phonecalls, you must also allow for time difference. If you are calling from San Francisco at 10 P.M., a friend of yours in Boston will be roused out of bed at 1 A.M. (This once actually happened to me.)

However, this is unavoidable inconvenience. At least, there are large areas within time zones where changes are unnecessary. Then, too, when you must make changes, you do it one hour at a crack, instead of 4 minutes here and 12 minutes there. Actually, no better system seems possible.

Time Zone Wriggles

If you look at a map of the United States in which the

time zones are marked off, you may be astonished at the twists and zigzags in the boundary lines. Theoretically, the zones are marked off by straight north-south lines, but this could cause inconvenience.

For instance the $82\frac{1}{2}°$ West Longitude line, which is the theoretical boundary between Eastern Standard Time and Central Standard Time, cuts right through the middle of the states of Ohio and Georgia. Now this could inconvenience the state governments, which would have to deal with two different times. Ohio and Georgia have decided to make Eastern Standard Time standard throughout those states. For that reason the boundary between Eastern and Central Standard Times falls exactly on the boundary lines between Ohio and Indiana and between Georgia and Alabama.

Other states do allow themselves to be cut in two by a time zone boundary. Florida and Michigan are examples. But when this happens, the states arrange to have the boundary follow some convenient dividing line rather than that of the theoretical meridian. Michigan runs the boundary through Lake Michigan and Florida runs it along the Chattahoochee River.

Whenever possible, nations try to keep themselves in single time zones for convenience sake. For instance, the boundary between the noon zone and the 1 P.M. zone is the $7\frac{1}{2}°$ East Longitude line. This cuts through the western bit of Germany and the eastern bit of France. However, France puts itself entirely in the noon zone (Greenwich Time) and Germany entirely in the 1 P.M. zone (Central European Time). Naturally, when a nation's boundaries change, its time zone boundaries frequently change also.

Only a few countries have time zone problems like those of the United States. Mexico has three zones, but most of it runs on Central Standard Time. Brazil has three, but most of its populated area is in the 9 A.M. zone. China has four, but most of its populated area is in the 8 P.M. zone.

One country that is worse off than the United States (because it stretches over more longitude) is Canada. In addition to the four time-zones the United States has, Canada has one that is more easterly than Eastern Standard Time and covers Labrador and the Maritime Provinces. This is *Atlantic Standard Time*. The north-western portion of that country is in a time zone to the west of Pacific Standard Time, so that Canada has six time zones altogether. (If we count Alaska, though, the United States has six time zones also.)

The champion in this respect, however, is the Soviet Union, which is divided up into no less than eleven time-zones. At Greenwich noon, it is 2 P.M. in Kaliningrad on the western borders of the Soviet Union, and midnight at the eastern tip of Siberia.

Some regions on Earth put themselves in between time zones in order to have their standard time closer to their local time. For instance, Newfoundland is at the eastern edge of Atlantic Standard Time. Consequently, it has established its standard time half an hour later than Atlantic Standard Time. At Greenwich noon it is 8:30 A.M. in Newfoundland (though it is 8:00 A.M. on the borders of Canada across the Gulf of St. Lawrence).

Again, Iran is half in the 3 P.M. zone and half in the 4 P.M. zone. Rather than subject itself to the inconvenience of two time-zones, it places itself entirely within a 3:30 P.M. zone. Astronomers all over the world use Greenwich time for their observations. This is sometimes called *Universal Time* as a result.

Daylight Saving Time

There is one refinement that, beginning in World War I, has been added to standard time. It came about as follows.

The working day in cities of nations like Great Britain and the United States starts at 8 or 9 A.M. and ends at 5 or 6 P.M. In order to get to work on time, people (who like to sleep as long as possible, naturally) will awaken no earlier than 7 A.M. And in order to get a full night's sleep of eight hours, they will go to bed at 11 P.M.

In the fall and winter this means that the 16-hour waking period begins, roughly, at about the beginning of day. It includes the entire daylight period and runs five to seven hours into the period of darkness. During those five to seven hours, a great deal of power is consumed for artificial lighting, but it can't be helped.

In the spring and summer, however, the sun rises earlier and sets later. Because it sets later, the 16-hour waking period only includes three to five hours of darkness. On the other hand, since the sun rises as early as 4 A.M. in Great Britain and 4:30 A.M. in the northern United States, two or three hours of early daylight are wasted during sleep.

Now then, if, in the spring and summer, businesses could only be persuaded to start an hour earlier, everyone would wake an hour earlier and go to bed an hour earlier. One of the hours of darkness would be replaced by one of the otherwise wasted morning hours of light. This would mean that 20 to 30 per cent of the power requirement for artificial lighting during the waking hours of darkness would be saved.

However, it is almost impossible to make people change their habits of rising and going to bed, and this particular change, what is worse, would have to be unanimous. All businesses and all people must agree to get an early start. If only some did and some didn't, there would be terrible confusion.

The only practical way to do the job would be to alter the official time. If, in the spring, you were to push the clock ahead one hour, habit would keep you waking up at 7 A.M. by the clock, even though it were 6 A.M. standard time. You would still go to bed at 11 P.M. by the clock, though it were 10 P.M. standard time.

If everyone did this, there would be one hour less of wasted sunlight during the morning sleep. There would be one hour more of sunlight during the evening. Power consumption would be cut. And, after the first day of adjustment, everyone would be living according to his usual habits. To be sure on the first night of moving the clock ahead, there would be a lost hour of sleep. This, however, would be gained back in the fall when it was time to move the clock an hour back again.

There were suggestions for this sort of change in summer standard time as much as ten years before World War I (An Englishman named William Willett fought desperately for it, beginning in 1907.) However, people usually think of time as something that mustn't be interfered with. Many think it is ordained by heaven, so that tinkering with it is sacrilegious. They forget (or never knew) that hours are entirely man-made, and that standard time is itself an interference with local time. Even many scientists felt it was useless to play games with clocks. They didn't realize that men followed clocks faithfully and could be made to change their habits simply by changing the clock.

So it wasn't until 1916 that anything was done and Willett, unfortunately, died in 1915, just too soon to see the victory. World War I was then reducing the amount of power that could be spent on non-essential purposes, so economic necessity won out over superstition. Germany, Great Britain and a few other countries began to shove the clock ahead in the summer.

This one-hour-ahead time is called *summer time* or *daylight saving time*.

Daylight saving time is not very useful in northerly countries where the day gets so long in summer that very little artificial lighting is needed anyway. It is also not very useful in tropical and sub-tropical countries where the day doesn't lengthen much in the summer, so that there is very little wasted morning sunlight to be concerned about. In agricultural communities, daylight saving time is not popular because farmwork must be done by the sun and fooling with the clock is just an unnecessary complication.

For these reasons, daylight saving time is not something the whole world could, or should, adopt. In the United

51

States it is customary to let various communities decide for themselves whether to adopt daylight saving or not. Most of the big cities of the north do. Almost all of New England and the Pacific Coast do. Many smaller communities don't.

This creates a certain confusion, since there is an hour's difference between daylight saving time and standard time. Two communities a few miles apart and within the same time zone may differ by one hour in time. Railroads are particularly plagued by this and often keep clocks in their stations which have two hour-hands. A black one shows standard time and a red one (pointing an hour ahead) shows daylight saving time.

Even when two communities both adopt daylight saving, confusion can be created if they don't go on and off at the same time. Once, a few years back, New York City stayed on daylight saving time till the end of October, while Boston went back to standard time at the end of September. During October, then, television shows (which followed the New York system) went on one hour late by the Boston clock. As I can personally testify, this irritated Bostonians nearly to death. Fortunately, it hasn't happened since.

Jumping a Day

If we go back to standard times and the time zones now, we will observe a curious thing as we circle the globe. Starting at Greenwich noon, June 5 (let us say), and moving our finger eastward on the globe, we pass the 1 P.M. June 5 zone, the 2 P.M. June 5 zone and so on. By the time we reach eastern Siberia, which lies in the zone to the east of $172\frac{1}{2}°$ East Longitude it is 12 midnight, with June 6 about to begin.

If, starting again at Greenwich noon, June 5, we had moved our finger westward about the globe, we would pass the 11 A.M. June 5 zone, the 10 A.M. June 5 zone and so on. By the time we reached eastern Siberia again to the west of 172½° West Longitude (approaching it from the other direction, this time) it is midnight with June 5 about to begin.

Notice what has happened. As one finger moves east from Greenwich, it passes across areas where it is later and later in the day. As the other finger moves west from Greenwich, it passes over areas where it is earlier and earlier in the day. By the time both fingers meet in eastern Siberia, it is midnight to both. However, the finger that moved east considers it to be a full day later than the finger that moved west.

The only solution is to establish a 24-hour difference at the 180° line. Just as you adjust your clock by one hour when you cross a zone boundary, you adjust the calendar one day when you cross the 180° line. The adjustment is one day backward if you cross from Asia to America and one day forward if you cross from America to Asia.

This does not mean you "lose a day" or "gain a day." It is just bookkeeping to balance the time books, so to speak. As one finger moved eastward around the world, it gained an hour every time it crossed a zone boundary. At the 180° line it would have to lose a day to make up for all those gained hours. The all-at-once loss of the day makes up exactly for the step-by-step gain of twenty-four hours.

A finger moving around the world westward would lose an hour every time it crossed a zone boundary. At the 180° line it would have to gain a day to make up for all those lost hours. The all-at-once gain of the day makes up exactly for the step-by-step loss of twenty-four hours.

All this is very well for fingers traveling about globes. An actual traveler moving about the Earth must deal with

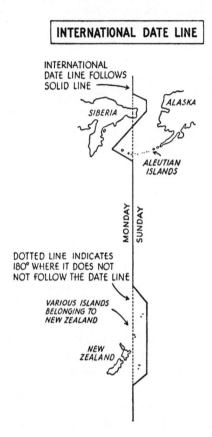

INTERNATIONAL DATE LINE

INTERNATIONAL DATE LINE FOLLOWS SOLID LINE →

ALASKA

SIBERIA

ALEUTIAN ISLANDS

MONDAY   SUNDAY

DOTTED LINE INDICATES 180° WHERE IT DOES NOT NOT FOLLOW THE DATE LINE

VARIOUS ISLANDS BELONGING TO NEW ZEALAND

NEW ZEALAND

the fact that the Earth is rotating and that time is changing. This obscures the way in which the day lost or gained at 180° balances the hours he has been gaining and losing at zone boundaries. If he were to check over his travels carefully and count up the hours lost or gained at zone boundaries and the days lost or gained at the 180° line, he would find, after he returned to his starting point, that they would balance out exactly. He would not have gained or lost a single second over his friends who had stayed at home.

The point at which the date changes in actual practice is not exactly at the 180° meridian everywhere. The Soviet Union, for instance, would prefer to keep all of Siberia on the western side of the line, even though the eastern tip of Siberia sticks over onto the eastern side of 180°. The United States prefers to keep the Aleutian Islands on the eastern side of the line, even though some of them are west of 180°.

As a result, the *International Date Line* has been established. It follows the 180° line about half its distance but zigzags here and there the other half to avoid cutting over land.

The fact that the 180° line cuts through less land than almost any other meridian on the face of the Earth was one good reason to make Greenwich the Prime Meridian. The Date Line, you see, would have to be directly opposite the Prime Meridian, wherever that was. A Prime Meridian in New York City, for instance, would run the Date Line right through the middle of Siberia, China, and southeast Asia. The nations affected would be very unhappy with that, since one part of the nation would always be in a different calendar day from another part.

The Inconstant Earth

By this time, it would seem that we have arranged the day and its divisions in perfect form. But nothing, after all, is perfect.

In recent years, mankind has built more and more accurate clocks based on regular motions of things that are even steadier than pendulums and springs. For instance, the *electric clocks* that are now so popular are based on the regular to-and-fro motions of a 60-cycle-per-second alternating current. Still better clocks, first built in 1955, measure time by the regular oscillations of atoms. Such super-accurate *atomic clocks* (also called *masers*) would not lose or gain as much as a second in hundreds of years. In 1960, one was built which would not lose or gain more than a second in 30,000,000 years.

Once man learned to keep time this accurately by means of mechanical devices, he could check once again on the regular, or supposedly regular, motion of the Earth. He did this by checking the length of the sidereal day from one day to the next. This is the length of time between successive crossings of the meridian by a particular star as I mentioned in chapter 2.

If the rotation of the Earth were perfectly steady, the length of the sidereal day would never vary (except for the fact that the star itself moves very, very gradually). However, it turns out that the length of the sidereal day is not perfectly steady but takes odd jumps, though very small ones. For instance, at one time the day might suddenly increase or decrease in length by a few thousandths of a second. No one has quite explained the reason for it. Of course, these erratic changes are not serious from a practical standpoint, especially since they cancel out in the long run, but they remain a fascinating problem for astronomers.

In addition to these erratic changes, there is also a smooth lengthening of the period of the day. This is the fault of the tides. The moon (also, less strongly, the sun) attracts the waters of the ocean by gravitational force. The ocean water humps up slightly under the moon and these humps (there is also one on the side of the Earth opposite the moon) move around the Earth as our planet rotates.

In shallow seas, like the Bering Sea or the Irish Sea, the moving water rubs against the sea-bottom. This serves as a kind of friction or brake on the Earth's spinning motion. The effect is not great but it is enough to cause the day to lengthen by 1 second, it is estimated, every 100,000 years.

Obviously, none of us need worry about that. However, it is curious to think that 200,000,000 years ago, when dinosaurs roamed the Earth, the day may have been half an hour shorter than it is now. (I say "may have been" because the size and shape of the oceans has varied on Earth during geologic times and the effect of the tides may have been greater, or less, in earlier ages.)

As far as the practical problem of everyday time-keeping is concerned, we are quite safe in considering the Earth's rotation constant. Astronomers and other scientists must, however, be cautious. Until 1960, the second was defined as 1/86,400 of the day. In that year, the definition was changed to 1/31,556,952.9747 of a tropical year, because the year (which I shall soon be talking about), varies less with time than the day does. This new second is called the *ephemeris second*.

CHAPTER 4

The Inconstant Moon

The Heavenly Body that Changes

For all their convenience, the day and its subdivisions are not enough in time-telling. There is a definite need for longer units. A man who is asked how long he was in the army could scarcely say 1402 days. Over periods longer than a few dozen days it would become tedious to keep track.

Primitive people must already have felt the need for something more than the day. Since the motions of the sun gave rise to the notion of the day, it may have seemed only natural to turn to the next most prominent heavenly body, the moon, and see what it would do.

The moon appears about the same size as the sun, but is much, much less splendidly bright. In one respect, however, it is far more astonishing than the sun. The moon changes shape! Even early Stone Age man must have noticed that much.

Anyone watching the moon would notice that there is a time when it appears just after sunset as a thin curved sliver of light. Its curve is toward the west, facing the departed sun. This is the *crescent moon*. ("Crescent" comes from a Latin word meaning "growing.")

And, indeed, the moon does appear to be growing, for

THE INCONSTANT MOON

LIGHT FROM THE SETTING SUN

PHASES OF THE MOON

CRESCENT MOON

NEW MOON

HALF MOON

GIBBOUS MOON

FULL MOON

EARTH

PORTION OF THE MOON ON THE SIDE OF THE DOTTED LINE FACING EARTH IS THE PORTION ACTUALLY SEEN the next night it appears a little higher in the sky just after sunset, and seems a rather fatter crescent. The crescent fattens each night and appears higher in the sky, too.

After about a week, the moon has become a semicircle of light, rounded on its western side, flat on its eastern. By then, it is just crossing the meridian at sunset and, naturally, it is called a *half moon*.

It continues to grow. The next night it has bulged out a little along the flat side and is a little west of meridian at sunset. It bulges out more the next day and in this shape is called a *gibbous moon*. ("Gibbous" comes from a Latin word meaning "hump," because the flat edge of the half moon seems to have developed one.)

The hump increases until, eventually, about a week after half moon, the moon is a perfect circle of light and is rising in the east just as the sun sets in the west. It is then the *full moon* and shines throughout the night (barring clouds, of course), setting as the sun rises.

But it doesn't stay full. The next night it rises some time after the sun sets and it is no longer quite round. It is slightly flattened on the western edge, which until then had been the round side. It is gibbous once more.

The next night the western edge is more flattened and the next night still more. What's more, each night it rises a longer time after sunset. Eventually, about a week after full moon, it doesn't rise until midnight, and is just crossing the meridian when the sun rises again. At that time it is a half moon once more, but now it is round on its eastern side, and flat on its western.

It continues to decrease and to rise later in the night. It turns into a crescent with its curve toward the east (where the sun is about to rise) and takes to rising shortly before dawn. Finally, it thins out and disappears entirely for a time.

And then once again, a crescent moon curved to the west appears just after sunset and the whole cycle begins again.

To primitive people it seemed as though the moon was born, grew to maturity, faded away and died. And then, miraculously, a new moon was born. In fact, that notion persists to this day in our name for the first glimpse of the crescent at sunset. We call it still the *new moon.*

The period from new moon to new moon was, for thousands of years, the natural "long" period of time to use. The time between new moons was about 29 or 30 days and this space of time is called, in English, the *month*, a word obviously derived from "moon."

But before we go any further, let's see what's really happening to the moon to make it behave this way.

The Moon and the Stars

Of all the visible heavenly bodies, the moon is closest to the Earth. It is only, on the average, 240,000 miles away. The next closest visible heavenly body (the planet Venus) is never closer than 25,000,000 miles to the Earth.

It is only the closeness of the moon that makes it appear so large, since actually it is a comparatively small body, only a quarter the diameter of the Earth. The sun is a hundred times the diameter of the Earth, but it is also some 93,000,000 miles away. By sheer coincidence, size and distance just cancel each other and both sun and moon appear the same size. The sun covers a piece of sky that is 32 minutes of arc wide. The moon covers a piece that is 31 minutes of arc.

The moon is so close to the Earth that it is firmly caught

in Earth's gravitational field. Of all the heavenly bodies that seem to move solemnly about the Earth, the moon is the only one that really does. (The motion of one heavenly body about another is termed *revolution* from a Latin word meaning "to roll around." The moon *revolves* about the Earth.)

The moon's revolution about the Earth is made difficult to see by the fact of the Earth's rotation. If the Earth were motionless we would be able to watch the moon's majestic motion from west to east about us. However, the Earth is itself moving from west to east and it makes the spin much more quickly than does the moon.

It is as though the Earth and the moon were two runners on circular tracks about a common center. The Earth runs about a very small circle and the moon about a much larger one. Although the moon is revolving two and a half times as fast as the Earth's surface is rotating, the Earth has so much less distance to go that it succeeds in overtaking the moon without trouble.

The result is that although the moon is really moving from west to east, the Earth's spin overtakes it and makes it seem to move from east to west. It rises in the east, moves westward, and sets in the west.

To see the moon's real motion, one must compare its position with the stars from night to night. The stars also rise in the east and set in the west. The stars, however, are so far away that their own motion takes many thousands of years to become noticeable. The stars circle about the Earth from day to day and month to month can therefore be considered a reflection of the Earth's rotation and nothing more.

So if we compare the moon's position to the position of some bright star, we cancel out the effect of Earth's motion. If the moon changes position in comparison to the star, that is the result of the moon's real motion only; nothing else.

Observing the moon, we may find that it is, let us say, just on the same meridian with a particular star at midnight of some night. At midnight the next night, behold! it is 13° east of that same star. In the course of 24 hours, the moon has drifted 13° from west to east in comparison to the star. The next night it is 26° to the east of that star.

In a little over 27 days, moving at that rate of 13° a day, it will have completed its motion through a full 360°. It will then be on the meridian again with that star. The exact time the moon takes to travel from a position in the heavens (using the stars as a guide) back to the same position is, on the average, 27 days 7 hours 43 minutes 11.5 seconds.

That is the time it takes for the moon to revolve about the earth and it is called the *sidereal month.*

However, the sidereal month is not the time from new moon to new moon and is not what primitive man would have called a month. (Remember that the sidereal day is not what he, or we, would have called a day either.)

It is the sun that marks a day when it crosses the meridian and not the stars. In the same way it is the relationship of the moon to the sun that marks the month actually used by man, and not the relationship of the moon to the stars.

Let's see why that is.

The Moon and the Sun

As the moon travels about the Earth, it manages, once a revolution, to get between the Earth and the sun. On occasion, it comes precisely between and then the sun is partly or even entirely hidden by the moon. If this happens, we have an *eclipse of the sun*, or a *solar eclipse*. When the sun is entirely hidden, it is a *total eclipse*. In most cases, however, the moon is slightly above or slightly below the sun so that the sun is not hidden.

Even so, the moon cannot be seen when it is between the Earth and the sun. The glare of the sun would drown it out even if it were shining, and in that position it is not shining. The moon, you see, is a cold body that shines only by the reflected light of the sun. When the moon is between the Earth and the sun, the half of the moon that is toward the sun, naturally, is experiencing day and is gleaming with light. That half is away from us. The half that is toward us on Earth and away from the sun is experiencing night. The part of the moon which we then would look at (if the sun's glare were to ·let us) is dark and cannot be seen.

However, as the moon, in its travels about the Earth, moves eastward from the sun, we can begin to see it. As the moon moves, the sunlit half moves to one side since it must continue to face the sun. We can just see a sliver of it around one edge of the moon and that is what we call the new moon. (The curve of the crescent must always face the sun, since that is where the light comes from. Artists who draw the moon with its "horns" facing the setting sun may know art but they don't know astronomy.)

The sun obscures the feebly glowing crescent of the moon, which is only visible when the sun is out of the sky. This means it can only appear after sunset. Since the moon is still quite near the sun, it must then appear in the sky, but a little above it, and quickly sets. (It is a little east of the sun and both are apparently moving westward as a result of the Earth's rotation, so the moon reaches the western horizon and sets a little later than the sun does.)

As the moon continues to drift eastward from the sun, we can see more and more of the sunlit half of the moon each night. When the moon reaches a point where it is at right angles to the line connecting Earth and sun 'that is, when the moon has completed one-fourth of its revolution) we can see exactly half the sunlit portion. Of the side of the moon facing us, the half toward the sun is glowing, the half away from the sun is dark.

The moon still continues to move eastward, growing gibbous as still more of the sunlit portion grows visible. At last it is on the side of the Earth almost directly opposite the position of the sun. (Occasionally, it is exactly opposite, in which case it enters the Earth's shadow and we have an *eclipse of the moon*, or a *Lunar eclipse* —the Latin word for "moon" being "Luna." In most cases though, the moon passes a bit above or below the Earth's shadow and is not obscured.)

When the moon is on the side of the Earth opposite to the sun, then the face of the moon that is toward the Earth is also toward the sun. It is entirely lit up and we have the full moon. Furthermore, since it is directly opposite the sun, it is at the eastern horizon when the sun is at the western horizon. Therefore the full moon is rising at sunset. And, of course, by the same argument it is setting at sunrise.

As the moon continues revolving, the lighted portion starts slipping away again about the other edge of the circle. The changes all happen again, but in reverse.

There are thus two half moons, one coming on the way to full moon and one on the way back to new moon. On calendars, the first is usually called *first quarter* and the second *last quarter*. It might seem puzzling to have a half moon called a "quarter." However, half the visible face of the moon is one quarter the entire surface of the moon, if you count in the unseen face on the other side.

An interesting point, by the way, is that as the moon revolves about the Earth, it spends exactly half the time in the daytime sky, and half the time in the night sky. Everyone has seen the moon in the daytime on occasion.

However, the daytime moon is drowned out in the sun's glare so that it never seems more than a feeble patch of light, while the night-shining moon is very prominent indeed for lack of competition. Furthermore, when the moon is in the daytime sky it is, on the average, less than a half-moon. When it is in the night sky it is, on the average, more than a half-moon. For those two reasons, we are much more conscious of the moon by night than by day and most people who observe the skies only casually would be ready to assert that the moon is in the sky only at night.

The Month We Use

A new moon occurs every time the moon, as it progresses from west to east among the stars, passes between us and the sun. If the sun moved with the stars exactly, this would happen every 27 days 7 hours 43 minutes 11·5 seconds (this being the sidereal month).

However, the sun doesn't move exactly evenly with the stars. For reasons I'll discuss later, it drifts eastward a trifle less than 1° every 24 hours in comparison with the stars. In the same 24 hours, the moon has drifted 13° eastward in comparison with the stars. In comparison with the sun, then, the moon has moved 12° eastward.

Since the moon gains less on the sun each day than it does on the stars, it should take longer for the moon to "gain a lap" on the sun than on the stars. To gain a lap it must move a full 360°. At the rate of 12° a day, the moon would gain a lap on the sun in 360/12 or 30 days. Actually,

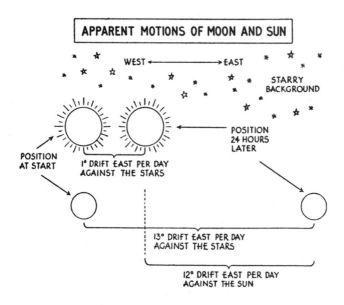

APPARENT MOTIONS OF MOON AND SUN

WEST ← → EAST

STARRY BACKGROUND

POSITION 24 HOURS LATER

POSITION AT START

1° DRIFT EAST PER DAY AGAINST THE STARS

13° DRIFT EAST PER DAY AGAINST THE STARS

12° DRIFT EAST PER DAY AGAINST THE SUN

the moon's gain is just a trifle over 12° a day, so it gains the lap in 29 days 12 hours 44 minutes 3 seconds.

That is the time from new moon to new moon. This is the period that was actually used as a measure of time for thousands of years. The task of keeping time was originally in the charge of the priesthood. A meeting of priests or other religious officials is termed a "synod" and it is such a group that determines when the new moon has arrived. The word "synod" could also refer to the meeting, not of priests, but of the sun and moon, for it is this meeting that produces the new moon and the beginning of the month. In either case, the period from new moon to new moon is therefore called the *synodical month*. It is also called the *lunar month* or the *period of lunation* (Luna being the Latin name for the moon).

To be sure, by the time the Babylonians had developed a reasonable astronomy, it was easy to tell in advance from previous observations of the moon, exactly when each new moon would come. Nevertheless, man is such a creature of habit that it was still customary for many more centuries to have someone pretend to watch the sky for the first appearance of the crescent at sunset.

In Roman times, for instance, the Pontifex Maximus (the high-priest) would go through the motions of watching for the crescent and at its appearance solemnly proclaim the beginning of a new month. The Latin word for "proclaim" is "calare" so the first day of each month was referred to as the *calends*. From this word, we get our own word *calendar* for a table indicating the various months.

The Romans broke up their months in a very illogical fashion. The day that came at or near the middle of the month (the 15th day in March, May, July, and October, and the 13th day in the other months) was termed the *ides*. (It was on the "ides of March" that Julius Caesar was assassinated.) The 9th day before the ides (counting the ides itself as one day) was the *nones,* which as we have already seen, is from a Latin word meaning "nine." The nones fell on the 7th day of March, May, July, and October, and on the 5th day of the other months.

Moreover, the Romans always counted backward from these key days. They would say that something took place on the 3rd day before the ides of such and such a month, or on the 2nd day before nones, or on the 12th day before calends.

68

THE INCONSTANT MOON

All this is uncommonly clumsy and none of it remains today, for which we should all be grateful. At the present time, we simply count the days of the month, in a straightforward fashion, from the first to the last day. We speak of the 15th of a particular month, or the 22nd or the 30th.

The Babylonians, however, broke up the month in a manner which does persist to this day. They took into account the changing shape of the moon and, particularly, its most noticeable forms. These, of course, were the new moon, the first quarter, the full moon and the last quarter. We refer to them as the *phases* of the moon, from a Greek word meaning "appearance."

The time between any two phases—from new moon to first quarter, from first quarter to full moon, from full moon to last quarter, and from last quarter to new moon—is, in each case, one-quarter of a synodical month. This comes to 7 days 9 hours and 11 minutes. The closest whole number is 7 and to many ancient peoples 7 was considered a particularly magical number, so the Babylonians divided the month into 7-day periods. (Perhaps 7 was considered magical because of its connection with the phases of the moon.)

This 7-day period we call a *week*, a word which has been traced back to a primitive Teutonic word meaning "change" (of the moon, of course). The modern German word for "change" is still "Wechsel."

The Days of the Week

Actually, the 7-day week is not a particularly good way of dividing the month, since it does not go into the month evenly. At the end of the fourth week (which ends on the 28th day of the month) the month still has a day or two to run. The fifth week, therefore, is divided. The first part includes the end of the month and the second part the beginning of a new month.

Perhaps this unevenness accounts for the fact that few primitive peoples followed the Babylonians in this 7-day habit.

One people that did, however, were the Hebrews. They adopted the week, probably, during the time they were captives in Babylon in the 6th Century B.C. Moreover, they gave the week a strong religious significance by making each Seventh day a holy day dedicated to God. On this seventh day no worldly business could be transacted. It therefore came to be considered a day of rest as well as one of religious dedication. Jewish people still observe this day, which is commonly called Saturday, but which in Hebrew is "Shabbat," from a Hebrew word meaning "rest."

The English equivalent of the word is *Sabbath*, which however is now applied by Christians to the day that is commonly called Sunday. The early Christians adopted Sunday, the first day of the week, as a special time for religious observances because it was on that day of the week that Christ was resurrected. (A few Christian sects, such as the Seventh-Day Adventists have re-adopted Saturday as Sabbath. These and the Jews may be lumped together as *Sabbatarians*.)

Once the week had become intimately connected with religious observance, it was naturally kept, even though it did cause confusion by not fitting the month exactly. Furthermore, since the early Christians spread their views over the civilized world, the week entered Greek and Roman civilization. The Greeks and Romans did not have the week in pre-Christian times. It was Constantine, the first Roman Emperor to be favorable to Christianity, who introduced the week into the Roman calendar.

Despite this connection of the week and religion, the days of the week have heathen names. The modern names arose in Roman times, for all that the Romans had no official week.

The Romans, it seems, placed each hour in charge of one of the prominent heavenly bodies. These included the sun, the moon, and the five visible planets: Mercury, Venus, Mars, Jupiter and Saturn. They listed these in what they considered to be the order of distance from the Earth, the most distant coming first. Thus: Saturn, Jupiter, Mars, the sun, Venus, Mercury, the moon. The body that was in charge of the first hour of a particular day was considered to be in charge of that day as a whole.

Saturn is in charge of the first hour of the first day so that is "dies Saturni" (Saturn's day). Jupiter gets the second hour, Mars the third, the sun the fourth and so on. If you keep this up, you will find the twenty-fourth hour is in charge of Mars, and the first hour of the second day is in the charge of the sun. The second day then becomes "dies Solis" (Sun's day). If you keep this up, you find the next days are, in order, "dies Lunae" (Moon's day), "dies Martis" (Mars' day), "dies Mercurii" (Mercury's day), "dies Jovis" (Jove's day —"Jove" being an alternate name for Jupiter) and "dies Veneris" (Venus' day).

You may have recognized the first three days as, in English, *Saturday*, *Sunday* and *Monday*. (Our week, however, begins with Sunday and ends with Saturday, because the Hebrews put "the day of rest" at the end and the habit has stuck ever since.)

The other days are still recognizable in French, for instance, as "mardi," "mercredi," "jeudi" and "vendredi," and in Italian as "Martedi," "Mercoledi," "Giovedi," and "Venerdi." However, the French call Sunday "dimanche," from the Latin word "dominicus" meaning "lord." It is the "Lord's day." We call Sunday the "Lord's day" in English, too, sometimes, but that is not its official name.

English inherits four of its names for weekdays from old Norse gods, these names being handed down from Anglo-Saxon, pre-Christian times. *Tuesday* is "Tiw's day," Tiw being the Norse god of war. *Wednesday* is "Woden's day," Woden, or Odin, being the chief Norse god. *Thursday* is "Thor's day," Thor being the Norse god of storm and thunder. (For those of you who have read the Norse myths, Thor's famous hammer, was really the lightning bolt.) Finally, *Friday* is "Frigga's day," Frigga being Woden's wife and chief goddess. (It is sometimes derived as "Freia's day," Freia being the Norse goddess of beauty.)

Despite Friday being named after such pleasant goddesses, many people feel it to be a day of bad luck. This may be because Christ was crucified on a Friday. (The anniversary of this event is observed on the Friday before Easter. This is called "Good Friday," which is a corruption of "God's Friday.") The number 13 is also felt to be unlucky. One theory is that it is because 13 people were present at the Last Supper, Christ and the twelve apostles. For that reason, Friday the Thirteenth is considered supremely unlucky and many people are quite nervous on such days. There is at least one Friday the Thirteenth every year and some years have as many as three. The year 1959 had three. However, this business of lucky and unlucky days is foolish superstition, and I hope the day will come when such beliefs disappear.

The Germans join us in this with some variation. Friday, they call "Freitag" ("Tag" being German for "day"). Thursday, they call "Donnerstag" ("Donner" meaning "thunder" in German and being an alternate name for

72

Thor). Tuesday is "Dienstag" after an alternate name for Tiw.

Strangely, though, the Germans leave out Woden, the chief. They call Wednesday "Mittwoch" which, in German, means simply "mid-week." And, of course, Wednesday is the middle of the week, so we can't quarrel with that.

Sunday and Monday are "Sonntag" and "Montag" in German, which is close enough. Saturday is "Samstag" but is often called "Sonnabend" which means "Sunday eve" in German. This is a peculiar hangover of the times when days began at sunset, so that what we call Saturday evening was, at one time, really Sunday eve.

The Sun, from West to East

The Seasons Go Round

As long as man was involved in a hunting society, the month was probably sufficient as a method of measuring periods of time longer than days and weeks. To be sure not all months were alike. Some might be hot and some might be cold. It might rain in some, snow in others and be dry in still others. This affected hunting, of course.

However, the situation grew much more serious once man learned to grow food; once he invented agriculture and settled down to be a farmer. There is advantage in agriculture. A farming community can support more men than can a hunting community. Farmers can settle down to live in one place; they are not forced to roam in search of game as hunters must. Cities become possible and civilization, both of which are impossible in a hunting community.

On the other hand, there is risk to agriculture, too. The greater the number of people and the more complicated the society, the more tragic the consequences should the food supply fail.

Now farming is much more dependent on the variation among the months than hunting is. If the crops are not planted at the right time, they are sure to fail. The farmer must know in advance when there is likely to be warm weather, with sun and rain for months to come, before he dare plant. He has to, in other words, become aware of the *seasons*. The very word "season" comes from a Latin word meaning "planting time."

In Europe and the United States, there are four seasons recognized. These are *winter*, *spring*, *summer* and *fall*.

Winter (from an old Teutonic word meaning "stormy") is noted for its cold weather which brings snow and ice. Nothing grows then. The trees are bare, the days are short, the nights long. The world seems dead.

Then comes spring, with the weather gradually warming. The days grow longer and nights shorter, the snow melts and green living things spring up out of the soil (hence the name of the season).

Then summer (an old Anglo-Saxon word of uncertain meaning), with its long days and short nights, and its heat. The world is in full bloom.

Finally fall, and the heat starts waning. Days grow shorter and nights longer. The ripe fruit falls from the tree (hence the name of the season) and the world seems to be slowly dying again. (Sometimes, fall is called *autumn*, which is the Latin name of the season.)

After that, winter comes and the cycle starts over again.

To the early farmers, it was apparent that spring was the time of planting, since the warm summer lay ahead. Autumn was the time of harvesting because by that time the crops were ripe; and besides, the cold of winter was on the way.

Spring was a joyous season because it meant the winter-death was over. Fall was a joyous season (if things had gone well with the crops) because a successful harvest meant certainty of food for the winter.

Agricultural communities usually have spring festivals and autumn festivals for that reason. The United States

75

has an autumn festival all its own in *Thanksgiving*. Originally, the Pilgrims, who were the earliest white settlers of New England, celebrated it as a day on which to give thanks to God for a good harvest.

Easter, although a religious holiday in observation of Christ's resurrection, gets its name from a pagan goddess of spring, Eostre, since the modern holiday comes at about the same time as an old spring festival.

The repeating cycle of seasons is called a *year* from an old word meaning "season."

It couldn't have taken long for the early farmers to notice that three new moons appeared in each season, so that each season might be taken to last about three months. It followed therefore that since there were four seasons in the year and each season lasted three months there were, therefore, twelve months in the year.

This notion has remained with us ever since. Almost all people adopted it. After all, twelve is a good number to work with, as I explained earlier in the book, and that must have helped out.

Naming the Twelve

Each of the twelve months of the year is given a different name, just as each day of the week is. The names we use are derived from the Latin.

The early Romans are supposed to have started the year with the spring season (a natural choice, it seems to me) and their first month was named Martius, after Mars, their god of war. The early Romans held Mars in special regard, so he was a good god with which to open the year. We call the month *March*.

Then came Aprilis, Maius, and Junius, which we call *April*, *May*, and *June*. April comes, perhaps, from a Latin

76

word meaning "to open" as that is the month when the buds open. May and June are from Maia, the goddess of growth, and Juno, the goddess of marriage and the family —good ladies to preside over the lovely spring months. (It is still considered good luck to be married in June, even though Juno is no longer worshipped.)

After this, the Romans simply numbered the months from five to ten, using the Latin names of the numbers, of course. These were, in order, Quintilis (fifth month), Sextilis (sixth month), Septembris (seventh month), Octobris (eighth month), Novembris (ninth month) and Decembris (tenth month).

In the time of Julius Caesar, who reformed the Roman calendar, the fifth month was named Julius in his honor and that has come down to us as *July*. The successor of Julius Caesar, his nephew Augustus Caesar, was also honored with a month. Sextilis was changed to Augustus and that has come down to us as *August*.

We have kept the other numbered months almost unchanged: *September, October, November, December*.

The Romans stopped numbering at the tenth month and perhaps they only had ten months at first. There is a legend that their second king, Numa Pompilius, added two more months, Januarius and Februarius, which we call *January* and *February*.

January is named for Janus, a two-faced god with one face looking back and one forward. This seems a good name for a month with which to end the old year and begin the new. Perhaps that is why the Romans at some early period shifted the year's beginning from March to January. Or perhaps they shifted first and then named the new first month appropriately. It's hard to tell.

In any case, the custom of beginning with January has

stuck with us to the present day and it has thrown the numbered months out of adjustment. September, the "seventh month" is now the ninth month. October, the

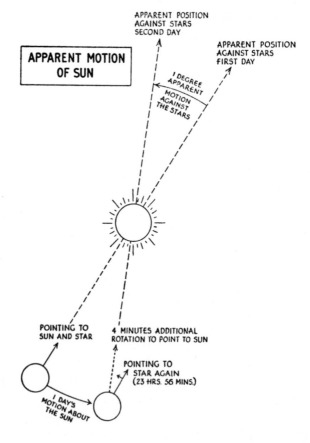

"eighth month" is now the tenth, and so on. Nevertheless, the names are not changed. Habit is habit.

Just to round off the derivations of the names of the

months, February comes from the Latin word "februo," meaning "to purify," because a "Feast of Purification" was held in this month.

However, it is time to turn back to the clock we live on, the Earth, and see what accounts for the seasons and the year.

The Slipping Sun

So far I have treated the Earth as though it were spinning in space but were otherwise motionless. This, of course, is not so. The earth has other motions. For one thing, it revolves about the sun, completing its revolution in just the time taken up by the cycle of the four seasons. The time of revolution of the Earth about the sun is one year.

Let's see what this means.

Imagine the Earth turning in space with a little rod sticking out of it which turns with it. At the start of a turn, the rod is pointing precisely to the center of the sun and to a star that we can imagine lying directly behind the center of the sun. Next, imagine the Earth making one of its daily rotations from west to east. The rod moves about with the Earth and at the completion of the rotation points once again to the star.

However, during the time taken up by the Earth's turn, it has moved a distance in its revolution about the sun. (This motion of revolution is in the same direction, by the way, as the spin of rotation. If you imagined yourself looking down on the Earth and sun from a great distance above the North Pole, the Earth would seem to be spinning *counterclockwise;* that is, in the direction opposite to those of the hands on a clock. The Earth would also be revolving about the sun *counterclockwise.*)

THE CLOCK WE LIVE ON

The motion of the Earth about the sun during the time taken up by a single rotation would make no difference to the star which is so far away. The much nearer sun, however, would, as a result of Earth's movement, seem to have slipped backward a bit in comparison with the star. (You may have observed something like this out of the window of a moving train. A house on the distant horizon is hardly affected by your motion but travels along with you. A house near the train seems to move backward in comparison to the distant house.)

Well, then, when the rod on Earth is pointing to the star again, the sun has seemed to drift a bit backward (to the east, that is). The Earth must turn for four additional minutes before the rod points to the sun again. This is the four-minute difference between the sidereal day and the solar day, which I mentioned earlier in the book. A clock can be designed to make 24 slightly short hours come to exactly one sidereal day. Such a clock keeps *sidereal time* or *star time* and gains 4 minutes a day, and one full day each year. A particular star is at zenith at the same time every day on such a clock.

In the same way the moon may begin its revolution about the earth at such a point that a line connecting the Earth and the moon will point toward the sun and to a particular star behind it. (The moon also turns about the Earth counterclockwise as seen from above the North Pole.) After a complete turn, taking about 27 1/3 days, the line drawn from Earth to the moon is again pointing toward the star. However, the sun will have drifted considerably backward because of the Earth's motion about it in that interval. (And the moon accompanies the Earth in the latter's travels about the sun.) The moon must travel in its orbit over two more days to line up with the sun again because of that backward drift. This is the reason

80

for the difference between the sidereal and the synodical months.

There is still another discrepancy that can be accounted for at least in part by Earth's revolution about the sun. As I've explained, the Earth rotates about its axis at an almost perfectly even speed. This is not true, however, of its speed of revolution about the sun.

The speed of revolution would be perfectly even, if the Earth rotated about the sun in a perfect circle, but it does not. Its path takes on the form of an ellipse, which is a kind of "flattened circle." This means that there are times when the Earth is closer to the sun (about 3 per cent) than at other times. When the Earth is comparatively close to the sun, it moves faster in its path about the sun than when it is comparatively far from the sun.

When the Earth is revolving more quickly than usual, the sun seems to drift eastward a little more than usual. It is delayed in its daily westward motion in the sky and crosses the meridian late. When Earth is revolving more slowly than usual, the reverse is true. The sun drifts eastward less and gets a headstart on its daily westward journey. It crosses the meridian early. This is one of the reasons why the sun sometimes reaches zenith a little before noon-by-the-clock, and a little after noon at other times. It is the reason we have to abandon the real sun and use a "mean sun" to calculate noon.

Mapping the Stars

The early observers of the sky had no notion, of course, about the Earth's revolution about the sun. They could and did, however, observe the difference between the sidereal day and the solar day. The former lasted only 23 hours 56 minutes. This means that a particular star which might cross the meridian at midnight one night, would cross it at 11:56 P.M. the next, and at 11:52 the next.

Naturally, the ancients lacked the kind of clocks that would measure the sidereal day by noting the exact time at which a star crossed the meridian one night and the next. However, as they watched night after night, the difference in times of crossing the meridian became obvious, even without clocks. After all, eventually a star that had been crossing the meridian at midnight or thereabouts during March, would be crossing the meridian shortly after sunset in June. You don't need clocks to see that the star is changing position with respect to the sun.

Each night, the stars would seem to slip farther to the west, all of them. The whole vault of the sky would seem to be doing it in one big piece (except for the sun, moon and planets).

The stars, of course, can only be seen, at any one particular time, in that half of the sky opposite to the half in which the Sun is. In the sun-half it is daytime and the stars are drowned out. However, as the vault of the sky slowly slips to the west day after day, new stars appear in the east just after sunset that were previously hidden in the sun-half. And, of course, old stars disappear into the dawn as they enter the sun-half.

Eventually, when the vault of the sky has slipped completely around, the original formation of the stars is seen again. Such a complete turn takes one year. By observing the night skies throughout one whole year stars can be seen, at one time or another, over the entire circuit of the sky.

It is possible, therefore, to make a model sphere and draw upon it the pattern of all the stars even though at any one time half of them are hidden by the sun. Such a star-map is called a *celestial globe* or a *celestial sphere*.

THE SUN, FROM WEST TO EAST

The word "celestial" comes from a Latin word meaning "heaven."

(It is not actually possible to see every part of the sky during the year, except at the equator. Elsewhere on Earth, there are always parts of the sky that are hidden throughout the year. The farther from the equator you happen to be, the larger the hidden part is. At the North and South Pole, fully half the sky is never seen. However, we need not be concerned with this at the moment.)

Each day it is possible to mark the position of the Sun on such a celestial globe. You can't actually see where it is against the stars because it drowns out their feeble twinkles and seems to shine alone in the sky. However, you can see the stars at night. By noticing which stars are overhead at midnight, you will be able to tell the position of the sun because it will be at the meridian directly opposite those stars. (This is no different from knowing that when it is midnight on the Prime Meridian, the sun must be directly over the 180° meridian, which is on the opposite side of our Earthly globe.) By measuring the sun's exact position above the southern horizon at noon, you can also find just where on its meridian it happens to be.

In this way the sun's position on the celestial globe can be pin-pointed each day. If this is done, the sun is found to make a complete circuit of the celestial globe in about $365\frac{1}{4}$ solar days. (There are $366\frac{1}{4}$ sidereal days in a year, exactly one more than there are solar days. In the space of a year, you see, the 4-minute discrepancy each day adds up to just one full day.

The ancients, I repeat, in following the sun about the sky had no notion that this was only an apparent motion resulting from Earth's revolution about the sun. They were sure that the sun was really moving, and circling about the Earth once a year.

It is rather difficult to measure the time of revolution accurately without careful observation. The ancient Babylonians figured it at only 360 days. They ought to have done better than that (since at the same time the Egyptians had figured it at 365) and perhaps it was a deliberate mistake.

The number, 360, you see, is a very convenient one so far as division is concerned. It can be divided evenly by 2, 3, 4, 5, 6, 8, 9, 10, 12, 15, 18, 20, 24, 30, 36, 40, 45, 60, 72, 90, 120, and 180. The number 365, on the other hand, can be divided by only 5 and 73. The Babylonians may have decided that the extra convenience of working with 360 was worth a small error.

Once the Babylonians settled on 360 as the number of days in the year, they may have used that as their reason for dividing the circle and sphere into 360 degrees. Such a division would mean that the sun would move eastward (in comparison to the stars) just 1° per day. Actually, since the sun takes 365 days, not 360, to complete its circuit, it moves 59 minutes 10 seconds (abbreviated 59′ 10″) each day, but that's quite close to 1° really since 1° equals 60′

Animals in the Sky

If you mark the line followed by the sun around the celestial globe, you have drawn what is called the *ecliptic* about it. The reason for this name involves the moon.

The moon's path against the stars can also be plotted on the celestial globe. Its line of travel is close to that of the sun's but isn't identical. The moon's path and the sun's path cross at two points on opposite sides of the celestial globe. These crossing points are called *nodes*, from a Latin word meaning "knot" (since a knot is formed where two lines join).

When the moon happens to line up with the sun (at

new-moon time) their two paths are sufficiently wide apart, generally, so that the moon is a little above or a little below the sun. If the line-up happens to be at one of the nodes, however, or in the close neighborhood, the two bodies occupy the same spot in the sky, so that the moon obscures the sun, either partially or entirely. This is an *eclipse*.

Since an eclipse can only occur when the moon happens to be near the sun's line of travel (at one of the nodes), the sun's line of travel is called the ecliptic.

(The word "eclipse," by the way, comes from Greek words meaning "left out" since during an eclipse of the sun, the sun seems to be left out of the sky with only a black hole where it ought to be.)

The path of the ecliptic passes through certain groups of stars that are still familiar to us today, more so than any other groups of stars.

You see, the early Babylonians who observed the sky, being imaginative, as all human beings are, were not content just to look at the stars as meaningless points of light. They joined them up mentally to form geometric patterns. We can scarcely avoid doing it ourselves when we look at the sky. There is the "Big Dipper" which consists of seven stars that would form a dipper if lines connected them, and a "Little Dipper" too. There is a "Southern Cross," a "Great Square," five conspicuous stars in the form of a W and so on.

The Chinese also made patterns out of the stars, as did the Greeks and others. It's the Greek arrangement that has come down to us. Being more imaginative than any other group of people before or since, the Greeks filled the sky with bulls, snakes, cups, lyres, and men, which they formed by connecting stars.

The groups of stars so formed into imaginary figures

are called *constellations* (from Latin words meaning "with stars").

Now the ecliptic cuts through twelve of these constellations. Why twelve? Obviously, this was arranged on purpose to allow the sun to pass through one constellation each month. These constellations are, in order (and giving both the Latin and English names): *Aries*, the Ram; *Taurus*, the Bull; *Gemini*, the Twins; *Cancer*, the Crab; *Leo*, the Lion; *Virgo*, the Maiden; *Libra*, the Scales; *Scorpio*, the Scorpion; *Sagittarius*, the Archer; *Capricornus*, the Goat; *Aquarius*, the Water-Carrier; and *Pisces*, the Fish.

Because so many of these constellations represent animals, this list is called the *zodiac* (from a Greek word meaning "circle of animals").

The line of the moon's journey about the globe, although it is not identical with the sun's, is close enough so that it also falls within these twelve constellations. In addition, there are five star-like objects, which are brighter than stars and do not twinkle, that also drift eastward against the starry background and travel about the celestial globe. These are the five planets visible to the naked eye: *Mercury*, *Venus*, *Mars*, *Jupiter* and *Saturn*. Each has its own line of travel but all remain within the constellations of the zodiac.

In ancient times, it was quite generally believed that the moving heavenly bodies, the sun, moon and planets, had some sort of influence on human beings. The sun's position in the zodiac at the hour of your birth was supposed to influence your character. You would be a "Taurus" or a "Leo" and that was supposed to mean something. The position of the moon and the planets at the time of your birth could also be used to forecast the events of your life, the time and manner of your death, your lucky and un-lucky days, and so on. This was called casting a *horoscope.* (The word "horoscope" comes from Greek words meaning "to observe the hour;" that is to observe the position of the planets, moon and sun at the hour of your birth.)

This sort of "fortune-telling" is called *astrology* and it is now known to be mere foolishness and superstition. Nevertheless, there are many people even today who seriously believe that the motions of points of light in the sky can affect them. Most newspapers run columns giving astrological predictions for the day, while a number of magazines are published which are devoted solely to astrology.

It is very disheartening to think that centuries of science and education have not succeeded in erasing such super-stition.

Yet I must not be unfair about this. The ancient and medieval astrologers, although much of what they did was nonsense, were forced to observe the skies very closely. Their observations made possible the advance of the true science of the stars, which is called *astronomy.* Some of the early true astronomers, like Johann Kepler, cast horo-scopes to earn a bit of money. That is no excuse for people to believe in astrology today, however.

CHAPTER 6

The Sun, from North to South

Lines Across the Meridians

But I have not yet explained the seasons. Let's go back to the Earth as it rotates and revolves and try again.

The Earth, as it rotates, spins about an imaginary line drawn through the Earth. This line is the Earth's *axis*; it emerges from the Earth at two spots on opposite sides. These are the poles; one is the *North Pole* and the other the *South Pole*.

An imaginary line drawn about the Earth exactly half way between the North Pole and the South Pole is called the *Equator*.

Now suppose the axis of the Earth were exactly perpendicular to the line connecting Earth and sun. In other words, we can imagine the Earth to be spinning upright, with the sun shining directly down upon the Equator.

To a person on the Equator it would then seem that on each day the sun would rise exactly in the east and set exactly in the west. At noon, it would be directly overhead.

To a person living north of the Equator, however, the sun would never appear directly overhead. At noon, it would be a little to the south of zenith—in the direction of the Equator. If you moved farther north of the Equator, the noonday sun would move farther south. If you

88

were near the North Pole, the sun would barely skim the southern horizon at noon.

The situation would be just the opposite if you were living south of the Equator. Then the noonday sun would appear north of the zenith (always in the direction of the Equator). The farther south of the Equator you are, the farther north the noonday sun. Finally, near the South Pole, the noonday sun would barely skim the northern horizon at noon.

The ancient Greeks, who lived north of the Equator (in the *northern hemisphere*, in other words) and who never traveled south of it, took it for granted that the sun was always south of zenith at noon. The great Greek historian, Herodotus, reported, however, that another early people, the Phoenicians, who were great sea-voyagers, had sent an expedition around Africa. He said that they claimed that at the southern end of Africa, they found the noonday sun to lie to the north of zenith. This was more than Herodotus could swallow and he sneered at the story.

Ironically enough, since the Phoenicians would never have made up that story (it would have sounded too ridiculous), they must have actually entered the southern hemisphere (that is, gone south of the Equator) and observed the fact. So the one thing that convinced Herodotus that the Phoenicians lied, convinces us that they told the truth.

But the Greeks did know that if you traveled north or south, the sun (and stars, too) shifted somewhat in the opposite direction. Star-watchers were therefore interested in their north-south position. They had already drawn imaginary meridians on the sky and on Earth from North Pole to South Pole. These were used to measure distance east and west, as I explained in Chapter 2.

Now they likewise drew lines on the sky and on Earth that ran perpendicularly across the meridians. This was first done about 300 B.C. by a Greek geographer named Dicaearchus. These were used to measure distance north and south. To do this, they began with the equator which was such a line. (This was some centuries after Herodotus, when the Greeks had learned a bit more about geography.) They then drew other lines parallel to the Equa-

CROSS-HATCHING THE EARTH

tor both north and south of it, until the poles were reached.

They allowed 90 such lines from Equator to North Pole and 90 more from Equator to South Pole. Each such line, running around the Earth, parallel to the Equator, was called a *parallel of latitude*. ("Latitude" comes from a Latin word meaning "side" because the lines had to be drawn from side to side on ordinary maps with north at the top.)

The distance between each of these parallels is one *degree of latitude*. Why 90° from Equator to the poles? Well, imagine yourself starting at the Equator and traveling toward the North Pole. When you have reached the North Pole, you have traveled 90°. Cross the pole and down the opposite side southward to the Equator—another 90°. Across the Equator and down to the South Pole—another 90°. Across the South Pole and up to the original starting point on the Equator—another 90°. The journey around the Earth via the poles has covered 4 x 90, or 360°, and, of course, it's 360° to a circle.

Each degree of latitude, as you might expect, is divided into 60 minutes and each minute into 60 seconds. Points north of the Equator are said to be so many degrees, minutes and seconds *North Latitude*. Points south of the Equator so much *South Latitude*.

By means of longitude and latitude, any point on Earth's surface can be located exactly. Longitude gives the east-west location and latitude the north–south location. Thus, New York City is 74° West Longitude and 40° North Latitude; Los Angeles is 118° West Longitude and 34° North Latitude; London is 0° Longitude (neither east nor west, of course, since it is on the Prime Meridian) and 51° 30′ North Latitude.

The Tipped Axis

Now just as the Earth is divided by the parallels of latitude, so is the sky divided. The latitude of the noonday sun in the sky would depend upon the latitude of the observer.

For instance (we are still supposing the Earth to be spinning upright, with the sun shining exactly over the Equator), to a person in Los Angeles at North Latitude 34°, the noonday sun would appear to be 34° south of the zenith. To a person in New York, who was 6° farther north than a person in Los Angeles, the noonday sun would appear to be 40° south of the zenith. To a person in London, still farther north, it would be 51° 30′ south of the zenith.

At the North Pole, which is 90° North Latitude, the noonday sun would be 90° south of the zenith. Since 90° is the distance from zenith to horizon that is just another way of saying that the noonday sun would be at the horizon.

For people living in the South Latitudes, the situation would be just the same, except that the noonday sun would be so many degrees north of zenith, rather than south.

However, if this were all so, with the Earth's axis directly upright with respect to the sun, day and night would always be equal, regardless of your position on Earth. The boundary of day and night would run through both poles and every point on Earth, as the Earth turned, would spend half its time in the daylight portion and half in the night portion.

But we know this is not so! Day and night are not equal at most times and in most places.

The answer to that is that the axis of the Earth is not upright as we have been supposing throughout this chapter so far. It is tipped! What's more, it maintains the direction of tip without any change you can notice throughout the year; that is, throughout Earth's revolution about the sun.

THE SUN, FROM NORTH TO SOUTH

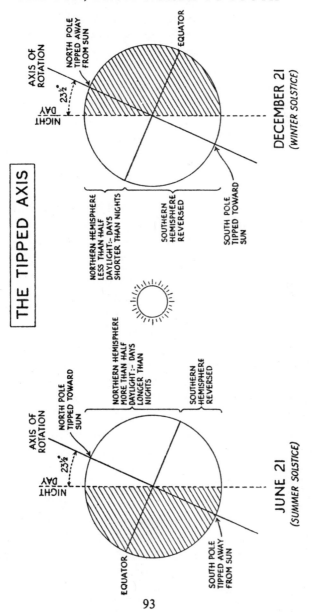

THE TIPPED AXIS

AXIS OF ROTATION

NORTH POLE TIPPED AWAY FROM SUN

23½°

DAY
NIGHT

EQUATOR

NORTHERN HEMISPHERE LESS THAN HALF DAYLIGHT – DAYS SHORTER THAN NIGHTS

SOUTHERN HEMISPHERE REVERSED

SOUTH POLE TIPPED TOWARD SUN

DECEMBER 21
(WINTER SOLSTICE)

AXIS OF ROTATION

NORTH POLE TIPPED TOWARD SUN

23½°

DAY
NIGHT

NORTHERN HEMISPHERE MORE THAN HALF DAYLIGHT :– DAYS LONGER THAN NIGHTS

SOUTHERN HEMISPHERE REVERSED

EQUATOR

SOUTH POLE TIPPED AWAY FROM SUN

JUNE 21
(SUMMER SOLSTICE)

93

This means that at one point in Earth's revolution about the sun, the North Pole is tipped a bit in the exact direction of the sun; and the South Pole directly away from it. The noonday sun is then not over the Equator but over some parallel of latitude to the north of it.

Starting at that point, imagine the Earth revolving about the sun. As the Earth keeps the direction of tip unchanged, the North Pole points less and less toward the sun as the Earth revolves. (It might help you if you were to push a knitting needle through an apple, the knitting needle representing Earth's axis. Keep that knitting needle tilted a bit and move the apple about another apple. Don't change the direction of tilt as you do this and see how one end of the knitting needle moves away from the central apple as you do so.)

Finally, half a year from our starting point, at the opposite side of Earth's path about the sun (its *orbit*, that is, from a Latin word meaning "circle") it is the South Pole that is tipped toward the sun and the North Pole that is tipped away from it. Now the noon-day sun shines over a parallel of latitude that lies to the south of the Equator.

As the Earth continues revolving, the situation slowly reverses itself. When Earth has returned to its starting point after a year in its travels, the North Pole is again tipped in the direction of the sun. The result is that, in the course of a year, each pole (alternately) seems to swing toward the sun, then away from it.

Even with the axis tipped, the Equator still gets its days and nights of equal length. Away from the Equator, though, it is a different story. When the North Pole is tipped toward the sun, regions north of the Equator have days that are longer than nights, while regions south have days that are shorter than nights. When the South Pole is tipped toward the sun, the reverse is true. Moreover the farther from the Equator, the greater the inequality.

As Seen From Earth

Now how does this look to someone, say, in New York City?

On June 21, the tilt of the axis is such that the North Pole is as far toward the sun as it can get. New York's sun

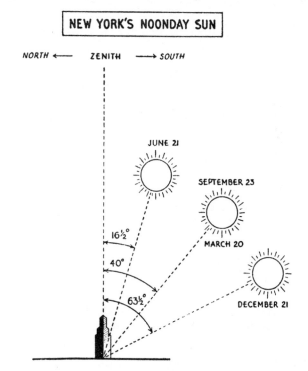

NEW YORK'S NOONDAY SUN

NORTH ←—— ZENITH ——→ SOUTH

JUNE 21

SEPTEMBER 23

MARCH 20

16½°

40°

63½°

DECEMBER 21

at noon is then quite high in the sky. It is only 16½° from the zenith. Since the latitude of New York is 40° north of the equator, the noonday sun should be 40° south of zenith, if it weren't for the tipping of the axis.

95

Actually, then, the tipping must amount to $40° — 16\frac{1}{2}°$, or $23\frac{1}{2}°$. That (or $23° 27'$, to be more exact) is actually the angle the Earth's axis makes with the vertical (that is, with a line perpendicular to the line connecting Earth and the sun).

On June 21, therefore, the sun is shining directly over the parallel at $23\frac{1}{2}°$ North Latitude (which is just about the latitude of Havana, Cuba). The sun never gets farther north at noonday than that.

In fact, after June 21, the North Pole begins to shift away from a direct tilt toward the sun and the noonday sun begins to be overhead more southerly parallels. The noonday sun doesn't reach quite as high on June 22 and falls even farther short on June 23 and so on. As this happens, the days grow shorter in New York and the nights longer.

This continues until September 23, when the noonday sun at New York is a full $40°$ south of the zenith. Since this is the latitude of New York, it means that the sun is exactly over the Equator. At this point, the day and night in New York (and everywhere else on Earth for that matter) are equal, 12 hours each. That is why the Equator is called that; it comes from a Latin word meaning "to make equal."

September 23 is called the *autumnal equinox*. "Equinox" is a Latin word for "equal night" and it is autumnal because September 23 ushers in the autumn.

But the Earth continues to revolve about the sun and after September 23, the North Pole is pointing increasingly away from the sun. The tipping of the axis now works to shift the noonday sun south of what it would ordinarily be if the Earth were upright.

again $40°$ from zenith in New York City. The sun is back

shifted the full 23½° south of what its position would have been if only latitude were considered. In New York, it is 40 plus 23½ or 63½° south of the zenith. It is only a little over ⅓ of the way up from the horizon. The day is the shortest of the year, the night the longest.

At that time of year, the noonday sun is directly over the parallel at 23½° South Latitude (which is just about the latitude of Rio de Janeiro, Brazil).

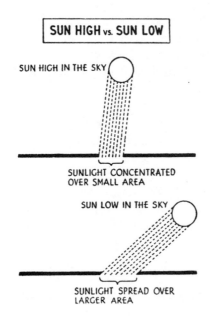

SUN HIGH vs. SUN LOW

SUN HIGH IN THE SKY

SUNLIGHT CONCENTRATED OVER SMALL AREA

SUN LOW IN THE SKY

SUNLIGHT SPREAD OVER LARGER AREA

But now the North Pole is tipped as far away from the sun as possible. As the Earth continues to revolve, the noonday sun starts climbing again. Days grow longer, nights shorter. At March 20, the noonday sun is once again 40° from zenith in New York City. The sun is back over the Equator and it is the *vernal equinox*. ("Vernal" comes from a Latin word meaning "spring" since this equinox ushers in the spring.)

The sun continues to climb still farther, the days continue to lengthen and the nights to grow shorter, until June 21 is reached and the whole cycle begins all over again.

If you were studying this with a sundial, the noonday shadow would shorten and shorten during winter and spring until June on 21 it would seem to stop and change direction. Then it would lengthen and lengthen throughout summer and fall until December 21, when it would again stop and change direction. (I mentioned this northward and southward shift of the shadow in Chapter 1, you may remember.)

These changes of direction on June 21 and December 21 are not sudden, actually. Through June or December, the change is very slight and it takes careful observation to tell on which day the shadow is actually shortest (because the noonday sun is farthest north) or longest (because it is farthest south). The days when the shadow seems to stop are called *solstices*, from Latin words meaning "stopping of the sun." June 21 is the *summer solstice* and December 21 is the *winter solstice*.

The Seasons Explained at Last

When the sun is high in the sky, it is warm for two reasons. In the first place, the sun's light hits the Earth at less of an angle, so it is spread out over a smaller area. The same light over a smaller area means a greater concentration of heat.

Secondly, the day is longer and the night shorter then than at other times of the year. There is therefore more time for the Earth to warm up and less time during the night for it to cool down.

For these reasons, in places like New York City or London, it is generally warmer between March and September than between September and March.

You may wonder why it isn't hottest on June 21, when the day is longest. The answer is that throughout July and August, the days are still longer than the nights (even though not so much as in June) so that Earth continues to heat up. It is July and August that are the hottest months in Europe and the United States.

The same argument in reverse holds for December 21. It is the shortest day but throughout January and February, the days are still shorter than the nights so that the Earth continues to cool down and those are the really deep winter months.

The situation is reversed in the southern hemisphere, of course. Our summer solstice is their winter solstice and vice versa; while our vernal equinox is their autumnal equinox and vice versa. When we are having long days and short nights with summer all about us, they are having short days and long nights with winter on hand. And, of course, the opposite holds true, too.

July and August are the months of snow and ice in Buenos Aires, January and February are the heat-wave months there.

As we travel toward the Equator, the noonday sun is higher, on the average, throughout the year than it is in places farther from the Equator. Moving south in the northern hemisphere (or north in the southern hemisphere) means, therefore, a move toward a warmer climate.

Naturally, the reverse is true, also. Moving away from the Equator and toward either the North or South Pole means a move toward a colder climate. There are, of course, other things affecting climate than merely latitude. It is cooler at high elevations than at sea-level anywhere. A position near an ocean has a climate that is different from another position at the same latitude that is far from an ocean.

Nevertheless, the general fact is that it grows hotter as you move toward the Equator and colder as you move away from it

And finally, then, the reason for the seasons of the year has been explained.

Poles in the Sky

If the imaginary axis of the Earth is drawn up through the North Pole and allowed to reach (in imagination) into the sky, its position among the stars can be shown on the celestial globe. This position is the *Celestial North Pole* and directly opposite it on the celestial globe is the *Celestial South Pole*. Midway between the two is the *Celestial Equator*. All the other parallels of latitude can be drawn on the celestial globe, too, as well as all the meridians of longitude.

The motion of the Earth about its axis makes it look as though the sky were rotating in the opposite direction, but about the same axis! This means that the Celestial North Pole (or Celestial South Pole) does not move with the rotation any more than does the North Pole (or South Pole) itself. (Or any more than the center of the hubcap moves from its place when an automobile wheel is spinning in the air.)

There happens to be a fairly bright star near the Celestial North Pole. It is called *Polaris* or, more commonly, the *Pole Star*. It is actually a little over a degree away from the Celestial North Pole but this isn't much. It is close enough so that, to the casual observer, it doesn't appear to move as the Earth rotates.

Since the Earth's axis always points in the same direction as it revolves about the sun, it always points to the same spot in the sky. This means that the position of the North Celestial Pole and the South Celestial Pole do not change during the year. Of course, at one point in its orbit, Earth is 93,000,000 miles to one side of the sun and at the opposite point it is 93,000,000 miles to the other side. So distant are the stars, however, that this shift of 186,000,000 miles in Earth's position during the course of the year makes practically no difference. (This is as though you were in New York and pointing your finger toward London. You would point in just about the same direction whether you were at the northern tip of Manhattan or the southern tip. London is so far away that moving from one end of Manhattan to the other doesn't make much difference.)

It is for this reason that the stars do not shift back and forth (to speak of) in the course of the year. It also means that the Pole Star keeps the same position not only during the course of a single night but during the course of all the nights of the year. That is what made the Pole Star so useful to navigators before the days of the compass. It always marked out which direction was north and from that all other directions were at once known.

The Pole Star is found at the tip of the tail of the animal pictured as the constellation *Ursa Minor*. This means "Little Bear," but bears have no tails and some people think of the constellation animal as a dog. The Pole Star was therefore sometimes called *Cynosure* in ancient times, from Greek words meaning "dog's tail." Because the Pole Star was watched so closely by navigators, "cynosure" has come to mean any center of attraction.

At the Equator, the North Celestial Pole is on the northern horizon and the South Celestial Pole on the southern horizon, and neither, of course, ever budges. The Celestial Equator runs east and west directly overhead.

If you were to travel north from the Equator, the North Celestial Pole would rise above the northern horizon and the South Celestial Pole would drop below the southern horizon. This rise and drop would be a degree for every degree you traveled.

At the latitude of New York City (40°), the North Celestial Pole is 40° above the northern horizon. The South Celestial Pole is 40° below the southern horizon. Since the stars make a daily rotation about the axis that extends through the Celestial Poles, it means that from New York not all stars rise and set. Those that are within 40° of the North Celestial Pole never quite make it down to the northern horizon, even at the lowest point of their daily circle. They never set. Such stars are called *circumpolar stars* (from Latin words meaning "around the pole"). The most prominent stars of this type are those of the Big Dipper.

Stars within 40° of the South Celestial Pole never quite make it up to the southern horizon even at the uppermost portion of their daily circling in the sky. Such stars are never seen at the latitude of New York City. The best-known of such invisible stars are those of the Southern Cross.

The farther north you go, the higher the North Celestial Pole climbs in the sky. As you go north there are more and more circumpolar stars and more and more invisible ones about the opposite pole. Finally, at the North Pole, the

North Celestial Pole is directly overhead. All the stars north of the Celestial Equator circle it at a constant distance from the horizon all about. None of those stars set. On the other hand, all the stars south of the Celestial Equator are forever invisible from the North Pole. None of them ever rise.

The situation, naturally, is just reversed if you travel from the Equator toward the South Pole. Then the South Celestial Pole rises in the sky and the North Celestial Pole dips below the horizon. In New Zealand, it is the Southern Cross that is circumpolar and never sets; and the Big Dipper that is never seen.

In one respect, the people in the southern hemisphere are less lucky than we in the north. There is no bright star marking the position of the South Celestial Pole as the Pole Star marks the North Celestial Pole.

More Zones on Earth

But now remember the Ecliptic, which marks the path followed by the sun against the stars. This line forms an angle with the Celestial Equator, crossing it at two points on opposite sides of the celestial globe. These points are called *equinoctial points* since it is when the sun is at those points that the equinoxes occur. The Celestial Equator is also called the *Equinoctial* for this reason. The ecliptic crosses the Celestial Equator at one point, moving from north to south, at the time of the autumnal equinox. It crosses at the other point, moving from south to north, at the time of the vernal equinox.

At its farthest north, the Ecliptic touches 23° 27' North Latitude. At its farthest south, it touches 23° 27' South Latitude. At these latitudes, the line of the Ecliptic seems to turn and to begin moving in the opposite direction.

After moving north to 23° 27′ North Latitude, it turns and starts to move south. After moving south to 23° 27′ South Latitude, it turns and starts to move north. This angle formed by the ecliptic with the Celestial Equator is called the *obliquity of the ecliptic* and it was first measured accurately by a Greek astronomer named Eratosthenes about 220 B.C.

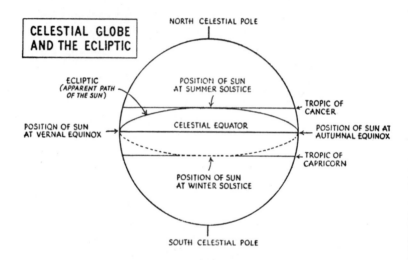

These two parallels of latitude, both on the celestial globe and on the surface of the Earth, are therefore called *tropics*, from a Latin word meaning "to turn." At the time the celestial globe was being worked out by the Greeks, the tropic north of the Equator was touched by the ecliptic at a point in the zodiacal constellation of Cancer the Crab. For that reason, 23° 27′ North Latitude is called the *Tropic of Cancer*. The tropic south of the Equator was touched by the ecliptic in the constellation of

Capricorn, the Goat. Therefore, 23° 27' South Latitude is the *Tropic of Capricorn.*

The region of Earth that lies between the Tropic of Cancer and the Tropic of Capricorn (with the Equator running along its center) is called the *Tropic Zone*, or, simply, the *Tropics*. It is the hottest portion of the Earth for reasons I explained earlier in the chapter.

At all points between the tropics, the sun is directly overhead at noon on two different days of the year. At the Tropic of Cancer, itself, the noonday sun is overhead only one day in the year, the day of the summer solstice, June 21. At the Tropic of Capricorn, the one day in which it is overhead is the day of the winter solstice, December 21. North of the Tropic of Cancer, the noonday sun is always south of zenith. South of the Tropic of Capricorn, it is always north of zenith.

As one travels farther and farther north, the noonday sun at the winter solstice (when it is lowest in the southern sky) is farther and farther from the zenith and nearer and nearer the southern horizon. At New York, the noonday sun on December 21 is only $26\frac{1}{2}°$ above the southern horizon. At London, it is only 14° above the southern horizon.

At $66\frac{1}{2}°$ North Latitude (a line which runs through Alaska, northern Canada, Scandinavia, and Siberia) the noonday sun on December 21 just reaches the southern horizon and goes no higher. There is a 24-hour period with no daylight. Still farther north, the period without daylight about the winter solstice is longer and longer. Finally, at the North Pole there is a six-month period without day.

(Actually, our atmosphere bends light rays—a phenomenon called *refraction*—and makes the sun appear above

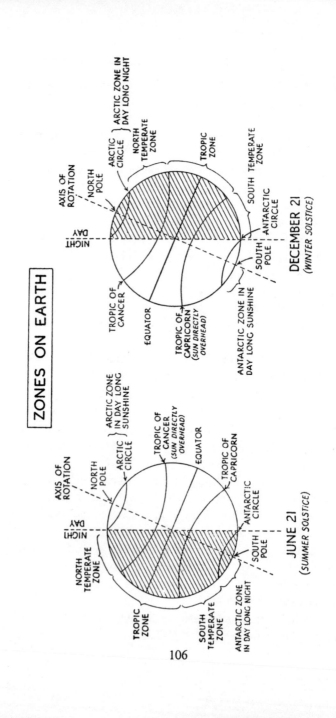

ZONES ON EARTH

JUNE 21
(SUMMER SOLSTICE)

AXIS OF ROTATION
NORTH POLE
ARCTIC CIRCLE
ARCTIC ZONE IN DAY LONG SUNSHINE
TROPIC OF CANCER *(SUN DIRECTLY OVERHEAD)*
EQUATOR
TROPIC OF CAPRICORN
ANTARCTIC CIRCLE
SOUTH POLE
DAY
NIGHT
NORTH TEMPERATE ZONE
TROPIC ZONE
SOUTH TEMPERATE ZONE
ANTARCTIC ZONE IN DAY LONG NIGHT

DECEMBER 21
(WINTER SOLSTICE)

AXIS OF ROTATION
NORTH POLE
ARCTIC CIRCLE
ARCTIC ZONE IN DAY LONG NIGHT
NORTH TEMPERATE ZONE
TROPIC ZONE
SOUTH TEMPERATE ZONE
ANTARCTIC CIRCLE
SOUTH POLE
DAY
NIGHT
TROPIC OF CANCER
EQUATOR
TROPIC OF CAPRICORN *(SUN DIRECTLY OVERHEAD)*
ANTARCTIC ZONE IN DAY LONG SUNSHINE

106

the horizon when it is really below it. This makes the matter a bit more complicated but for the purposes of this book, we will ignore refraction.)

The situation is reversed at the time of the summer solstice. At $66\frac{1}{2}°$ North Latitude, on June 21, the sun never rises higher than $47°$ above the southern horizon, which puts it only halfway to the zenith. However, as it travels westward, it veers about to the north and never quite sets. At midnight it just skims the northern horizon and starts climbing again. There is day for a continuous 24-hour period. The farther north you go, the longer the period of continuous daylight about the summer solstice. Finally, at the North Pole, when there isn't a six-month night, there is a six-month day.

The land north of the $66\frac{1}{2}°$ North Latitude line is called the "Land of the Midnight Sun." It might also be called the "Land of the Noonday Night."

The same happens in those regions of the Earth south of $66\frac{1}{2}°$ South Latitude, except that there the continuous night periods occur around June 21 and the continuous day periods around December 21.

We call the northern regions "arctic" for an interesting reason. As I explained earlier, traveling north meant that the North Celestial Pole rose higher in the sky. This, in turn, meant that the Pole Star and stars near it rose high. These stars make up several constellations including those we call the Big Dipper and the Little Dipper. (The pole Star is the brightest star of the Little Dipper.)

Where we see dippers, the Greeks saw bears. They called the Big Dipper, the Great Bear (*Ursa Major* in Latin). The Little Dipper was the Little Bear (*Ursa Minor* in Latin). Traveling north, then, meant the two bears, great and little, rose in the sky and seemed to dominate it more.

Since the Greek word for "bear" is "arktos," they called the northern regions "arktikos" and that has come down to us as "arctic."

The line of $66\frac{1}{2}°$ North Latitude, which encircles the northern part of Earth's globe, is called the *Arctic Circle*, therefore. The region within it is the *Arctic Zone*.

The Greek word for far southern regions was "antarktikos," meaning "opposite to the bear." So the line of $66\frac{1}{2}°$ South Latitude is the *Antarctic Circle*. The region within that circle is the *Antarctic Zone*.

The Arctic Zone is mostly ice-covered water, but the Antarctic Zone is almost filled with ice-covered land, a continent named *Antarctica*.

Between the Arctic Circle and the Tropic of Cancer (that is, between $23\frac{1}{2}°$ and $66\frac{1}{2}°$ North Latitude), there is a region of Earth that never sees the sun at zenith. It never sees the sun at midnight, either. It is not as hot as the tropics on the average, nor as cold as the arctic. This is the *North Temperate Zone*. (The word "temperate" means "to avoid extremes.")

Similarly the region between the Antarctic Circle and the Tropic of Capricorn is the *South Temperate Zone*. (These climatic zones which run east and west on the Earth's surface, must not be confused, by the way, with the time-zones, which run north and south—see Chapter 3.)

Now all these divisions of the Earth, these differences in temperature, climate, and the behavior of the day and night, are consequences of the tipping of the Earth's axis of rotation, and of its revolution around the sun.

If that is all clear now, and I hope it is, we can go back to the measurement of the year and the very peculiar difficulties it gave rise to in ancient times.

CHAPTER 7

Reconciling Sun and Moon

The Birth of the Sun

I have said that the Babylonians counted 360 days to the year, either because of a mistake in measuring or out of the deliberate choice of a convenient number. I also mentioned that the Egyptians did better and came up with the figure 365.

Egypt does not have seasons like ours but has a desert and sub-tropical climate. It has no real winter, no rainy season. There weather is so monotonous that it might seem unlikely that its people would care about the sun's shifting position through the year. How is it, then, that they studied the sun so carefully as to find out how long it took to make a circuit of the sky.

The Egyptians, as it happens, do have one kind of season that is all-important. The Nile River is the only source of water in Egypt and it is all that has enabled Egypt to support its dense population for the last 6,000 years and more. Once a year, the rains pour down in east central Africa, where lie the sources of the Nile. The waters of the Nile rise and in mid-July a river flood makes its way to the Mediterranean. The Egyptian farms are covered for a while but, when the flood recedes, it leaves behind rich new fertile soil.

It was necessary for the Egyptians to learn when the

flood was due. It always came when the sun was in a particular part of the sky, as it turned out, so the Egyptian astronomers began to study the sun.

They may have discovered that the year was 365 days long as early as 4200 B.C., though most historians now favor 2481 B.C. as the date. This was a great discovery and there was no improvement on this value for over 400 years.

The importance of the sun as an indicator of the flood was obvious to the Egyptians and they worshipped it as a god. About 1370 B.C., the Egyptian Pharoah, Ikhnaton, tried to abolish all the many strange gods the Egyptians worshipped in addition to the sun. He tried to make the sun the only god of all the land. It was the first known attempt to establish the worship of a single god. However, the ancient Egyptians were the most conservative of any people we know. They resisted any change of their old ways and when Ikhnaton died, his new religion was forgotten.

The sun had a more powerful hold on more northern people, however. To them, the sun brought not just an annual flood. It brought relief from ice and cold. It brought warmth and the green growing things of spring.

From an early time, the primitive people of Europe knew about the movements of the sun. Perhaps they picked it up from Egypt by some roundabout method. Perhaps they worked it out themselves. The ancient ruins at Stonehenge, England, for instance (which consist of tremendous rocks standing on edge in a double circle—except for those that have fallen down) were originally a tribute to the sun. A line connecting the center of the circle with two markers outside of it cuts the eastern horizon just at the point where the sun rises at the summer solstice.

RECONCILING SUN AND MOON

One can imagine primitive man anxiously watching the lengthening shadow of the noonday sun as it sank in the southern sky farther and farther each day. The days shortened and grew long and bitter. Would the sun sink for ever and vanish out of sight? Would the world come to a frozen end then?

Then comes the day when the shadow grows no more; when it turns and begins to shorten. This is the winter solstice and was often the occasion for a great celebration. Even though it will continue to grow colder, even though three months of winter lie ahead, the people know that the sun is returning. Someday, they now know for certain, it will be spring.

Even as late as the Roman Empire, there was a sun-religion called Mithraism. It originated in Persia and its chief figure was the god Mithras who represented the sun. In his honor there was a great festival at the time of the winter solstice.

Christianity was also rising in popularity then. About 300 A.D., the great festival of Christmas, marking the birth of Christ, was established. It, too, was set at about the time of the winter solstice by Constantine and is still celebrated on December 25.

It may be, in fact, that one reason for the shift of the beginning of the Roman year from March 1 (near the vernal equinox) to January 1 was that the latter date was near the winter solstice. If so, we still, to this day, begin each new year at the time of the birth of the sun.

Trouble with the Moon

There is no question, then, but that ancient civilizations and even quite primitive people knew about the behavior of the sun. They even had a pretty good idea of the length of the year.

There was only one trouble. Almost all ʳeoples already had a system of time-telling which was based on the moon, as I described in Chapter 4. This is the so-called *Lunar Calendar*, in which each month starts at the new moon. This was too convenient to abandon easily.

For one thing, the movements of the sun, although very important, could only be judged properly with instruments that can measure the angle between the sun and the horizon. That was all right for astronomers but not for ordinary people. Every shepherd, however, and every housewife, could see the changes in the moon with his or her own eyes. It was difficult to argue average people into giving up something simple that they could see for themselves for something complicated they had to take other people's words for.

And yet the Lunar Calendar had its serious problems. The synodical month (from new moon to new moon) is just about 29½ days long. Since a month of 29½ days would be difficult to handle, the usual custom was to make one month 29 days long, the next 30, the next 29, and so on alternately. The *Lunar Year* would consist, therefore, of six months of 29 days and six of 30 days. The total length would be 354 days.

The length of the Lunar Year is thus 11 days less than the length of the Solar Year. (The Solar Year or *Seasonal Year* is also called the *Tropical Year* because it is the time from the day when the sun is over the Tropic of Capricorn to the day when it is once more over it—from winter solstice to winter solstice, in other words.)

You might think: What's 11 days out of 365?

Ah, but it mounts up. After two years, the Lunar Year

is 22 days short of the Solar Year. After three years, it is a full month short.

And the trouble is that the seasons follow the Solar Year strictly. If you follow the Lunar Year instead, then trouble begins. At the start, planting time might be in March and harvest in October. Three years pass and the Lunar Year loses a month against the Solar Year; that is, against the seasons. Now planting time comes in April and harvest time in November. Another three years and there is another month's difference. After 16 years or so, July and August would coincide with winter; January and February with summer.

What to do? If you tried to make 13 Lunar Months to the year, you would have a very inconvenient number to deal with, since 13 cannot be divided evenly by any number. Besides, 13 Lunar Months comes out to 383 days which is 18 days more than the Solar Year and that is even worse than before.

There have been several attempted solutions to this problem.

The first and simplest solution is to ignore the whole thing. The ancient Assyrian calendar did that. The Mohammedan calendar still does that today. The Mohammedan calendar is very primitive, in fact. It starts the day at sunset, and divides day and night into 12 hours, so that the length of the hour varies with the season (see Chapter 1).

The Mohammedan year consists of 12 Lunar Months, alternately 30 and 29 days. Since the synodical month is actually 44 minutes longer than $29\frac{1}{2}$ days, such a calendar lags behind the moon by 88 minutes at the end of two such months. After twelve Lunar Months (that is, one Lunar Year), it lags behind by 44 x 12 or 528 minutes. This is about 8·8 hours.

In 30 Lunar Years, this lag comes to 8·8 x 30 or just about 11 days. To make up for this, 11 out of every 30 Mohammedan years (according to a certain fixed pattern) are given an extra day and are a total of 355 days long.

Such an added day, meant to help the calendar catch up with the movements of a heavenly body, is called an *intercalary day*. ("Intercalary" means "between the calendar." The day is inserted, in other words, between two days of the ordinary calendar.)

No attempt, however, is made to catch up with the sun. Intercalary months existed before Mohammed, but the early Mohammedans abolished them. Now the Mohammedan calendar is allowed to lag behind the sun 11 days each year. By the time 33 years have passed, it has lost an entire year.

This means that every 33 years, the various seasons of the year work their way through the entire calendar. It also means that a particular Mohammedan holiday might come in the cold season one year and in the warm season in another year.

Forcing the Moon into Line

However, although the Mohammedans seem to be getting along, most people apparently found a pure Lunar Year, with its shifting seasons, unbearable. The Hebrew Calendar, for instance, also uses the Lunar Month (alternately 29 and 30 days) but is not allowed to fall behind the sun permanently.

The Hebrew years are counted off in groups of 19 (because 19 solar years are almost exactly 235 Lunar Months, so that in such a time interval sun and moon are almost back in step) and out of each group of 19,

an additional month (*intercalary month*) was added in
the 3rd, 6th, 8th, 11th, 14th, 17th and 19th years. Out
of each 19 years, in other words, 12 were made up of
12 Lunar Months and 7 were made up of 13 Lunar
Months. The total number of days in 19 such years is
6936, but the Jewish calendar actually arranges matters
so as to have the average number come out to 6939.7.
The total number of days in 19 Solar Years is actually
6939.6 and the discrepancy amounts to only one day in
200 years. Even closer fits can be made by using 76 or
even 345-year cycles, but no calendar tries anything so
complicated.

(This way of keeping the Lunar Year even with the
sun was invented by the Babylonians about 500 B.C.
and was adopted by the Greeks. The Jews adopted it in
A.D. 358.)

On the whole, the Hebrew calendar kept up well with
the sun. It was never allowed to fall more than 22 days
behind the sun or to get more than 8 days ahead of it. The
result was (and is, for Jews use the Hebrew calendar for
religious purposes to this day) that individual months
shifted back and forth a bit, but that's all. They don't
move through the entire year as the Mohammedan months
do.

The main trouble with the Hebrew calendar, which is a
mixed *Lunar-Solar Calendar* is that it is unusually complicated. And incidentally, the intercalary month was
considered unlucky by some people because it upset the
even order of months. Since the intercalary month is the
thirteenth in the year, this may be one of the reasons
that makes thirteen seem such an unlucky number to
superstitious people.

It was the Egyptians who thought of what to us seems
115

the sensible solution. They abandoned the Lunar Month. They had 12 months in their year, but they let the first eleven months have 30 days each (divided into three groups of ten days) and the twelfth month 35. This came to a total of 365 days. Now the year kept up with the sun, or almost did, anyway. This is a pure *Solar Calendar*.

This, of course, meant that the new moon no longer came on the first day of each month. If it shone on the first day of the first month, it would appear again on the 30th day of that same month, then on the 28th day of the next month, the 27th day of the month after, the 25th day of the month after and so on. Just as the seasons wander through the year in the Lunar Calendar, so do the phases of the moon wander through the month in the Solar Calendar.

A month of the Solar Calendar is called a *Calendar Month*. It is an artificial month, designed to fit the motions of the sun. Although it is still called "month," it no longer matches the phases of the moon.

The Egyptian invention of the Solar Calendar was a vast improvement in the art of time-keeping. The seasons remained steady and the Egyptian calendar, unlike the Hebrew calendar, was the same each year. The Hebrew calendar was always surprising people with intercalary months, but people using the Egyptian calendar knew exactly what to expect every year.

You may wonder why people with Lunar or Lunar-Solar Calendars didn't instantly drop them when they learned of the Solar Calendar. Well, they didn't. It took thousands of years for the Solar Calendar to be adopted, and in some ways, the Lunar Calendar persists to this day in even the most advanced countries.

One explanation is, of course, habit. Another, however,

is the importance of the Lunar Calendar in connection with religion.

The Moon Hangs On

The phases of the moon have had a kind of superstitious importance to people till quite recent times. Farmers thought it was important to plant the seeds of certain plants at particular phases of the moon. Other people believed that magic was particularly effective on the night of the new moon, or that people were stricken mad by the full moon (hence the word "lunatic") or that werewolves prowled then.

All this is nonsense. The phases of the moon have no effect on Earth except to give more light on some nights than on other nights and to help mankind keep time. However, it shows how feelings about the importance of the moon linger on.

Imagine how much stronger are the feelings concerning religious observances that are tied to the phases of the moon. Time-keeping, as I have said before, was, until modern times, always in the charge of the priesthood. The Hebrew priests, for instance, when announcing the new month as a result of having observed the first glimmer of the crescent moon, naturally made a kind of religious observance out of it. Other religious holidays fell upon certain days of the month, meaning a certain number of days after the new moon.

To adopt a Solar Calendar might mean then that holy days would have to be celebrated on a particular day of the calendar month. But remember that the phases of the moon wander through the calendar month. The holiday, therefore, would in that case come at a different time after the new moon each year.

This thought bothered people greatly. Human beings always hate to alter special days in any way. Some years ago, for instance, President Franklin D. Roosevelt tried to move Thanksgiving one week forward to give merchants an extra week to prepare for Christmas. There was an unbelievable howl about it. Some states refused to budge, while others celebrated two Thanksgivings.

Now this concerned a holiday that is a purely American invention and is not part of any religion. It wasn't even celebrated officially throughout the nation until 1864. You can imagine, then, how people would feel about altering days that were connected with their religion for hundreds and even thousands of years.

Another possibility would be to adopt a Solar Calendar for ordinary use, but to keep holidays by the old Lunar Calendar. This would mean that the day on which holidays were celebrated would shift from year to year according to the Solar Calendar.

This is actually the case with Jewish holidays, as observed by Jews in the modern nations of the west. For instance, Rosh Hashonah (New Year) may fall on September 20 and 21 one year, on September 10 and 11 the next, and on September 28 and 29 the one after that. Passover might begin on March 31 one year, on April 18 the next and April 7 the one after that.

This keeps the holy days in line with the moon and doesn't offend the religious feelings of Jews, but there is obviously an inconvenience to it. The average American Jew doesn't know when a holy day will come unless he looks it up on a special calendar, or in the World Almanac.

Either way there are problems. Most people, therefore, held on to their Lunar calendars and ignored the Solar Calendar as long as they could.

RECONCILING SUN AND MOON

The earliest Christians were mostly of Jewish origin and used the Lunar Calendar. Many of the Christian holy days, like the Jewish holy days, are therefore "movable." They do not fall on the same calendar day from year to year.

One exception to this is Christmas, which does not follow the moon, but is celebrated on the same calendar day, December 25, each year. Christmas, however, is a latecomer to the list of Christian holy days. It wasn't celebrated regularly until some time after 300 A.D. By then, most Christians were of non-Jewish origin and quite at home with the Roman Calendar, which was a Solar Calendar borrowed from Egypt.

As the Roman Calendar came into use, though, the early Christians had to figure out a way to handle the "movable" holy days. It was too late to tamper with them.

The "movable" holy days all depended (and still do) on Easter. Once the date for Easter is fixed, all the other holy days can be placed so many days or weeks before Easter or after Easter. Consequently, it was necessary to evolve methods for fixing the date of Easter.

This was done by allowing Easter to fall upon the first Sunday after the first full moon coming on or after March 21 (the vernal equinox). The complication is that the full moon is not the real full moon anyone can observe in the sky. It is, instead, an imaginary full moon, called the *Paschal full moon,* which may come a day before or after the real full moon. (The word "paschal" comes from the Hebrew "pesach" meaning "passover." Easter comes at the Jewish passover season and this word is a holdover from the time when most Christians were of Jewish origin.)

The Paschal full moon must be calculated and this is done in a rather complicated fashion we needn't go into here. I'll just mention that it involves giving each year a "Golden Number" and a "Dominical Letter" and that both are used in the calculations.

The result is that Easter can fall as early as March 22 and as late as April 25. For instance, Easter fell on March 23 in 1913 and will fall on that date in 2008 once again. It was celebrated on April 25, 1943, and we will have another chance (or our grandchildren will) to have such a late Easter in 2038.

Once the date of Easter is known, other holy days can be fixed. Ash Wednesday, for instance, comes 40 days earlier than Easter (not counting Sundays). The time between is Lent. (Lent falls mostly in the month of March, and the old Anglo-Saxon name for March was "lenct" meaning "spring." Hence the name "Lent.")

The British Parliament in 1928 thought it might try to reduce the fluctuation of Easter by adjusting it to the Solar Calendar somewhat. They voted that Easter be set on "the first Sunday after the second Saturday in April." This would mean that Easter would always fall somewhere between April 9 and April 15. However, this naturally came to nothing. Even now, 6,000 years since the invention of the Solar Calendar, the grip of the moon is too strong to be shaken.

The Untouchable Week

There is another calendar complication that depends on the fact that the week doesn't go evenly into the year.

The number of days in the year, 365, if divided by 7, gives 52 and a remainder of 1. This means that there are 52 weeks plus one day in the year.

Consequently, if one year begins on a Sunday, the next begins on a Monday because of that extra day. The one after begins on a Tuesday and so on. (Leap Year complicates this, but I'll discuss that later in the book.) If a holiday occurs on a fixed day of the month, it can never come on the same day of the week two years running. Thus if Independence Day (July 4) falls on a Friday one year, it will fall on a Saturday the next.

Independence Day came on a Sunday in 1954. Because it is not considered proper to celebrate a non-religious holiday on a Sunday, it was celebrated on the following Monday (July 5) in that year. This interference with Sunday is one example of the inconveniences of a shifting day of the week for holidays.

Then, too, there is this. If July 4 falls on a Saturday, there is an ordinary 2-day weekend. If it falls on Friday, Sunday or Monday, there is a long 3-day weekend which is important to today's motoring population (and a cause of sharp rises in the automobile accident rate). If it falls on Tuesday, Wednesday or Thursday, it breaks up the work week inconveniently.

For that reason, some people have suggested that holidays always be celebrated on the nearest Monday to their actual date. There will always be a long weekend and an unbroken work week, though a somewhat shorter one. However, this notion is not likely to be accepted. People wouldn't feel right about celebrating the 4th of July on the 7th of July, just because the 7th was a Monday.

Still, there are holidays which are allowed to fall on a particular day of the week, regardless of the actual date of that day.

Thanksgiving, for instance, was proclaimed for the last Thursday in November by President Lincoln and by those who followed him until Roosevelt's time. Roosevelt tried to push it a week ahead in those years when there were five Thursdays in November but he left it on Thursday.

Labor Day is established as falling upon the first Monday in September and may come any time between September 1 and September 7. This insures a 3-day weekend every time. Election Day is the day after the first Monday in November so that it falls between November 2 and November 8 and always comes on a Tuesday.

It has been suggested by some people that the year be made exactly 52 weeks in length and that the 365th day, December 31, be just a general day (possibly called *Year Day*) with no day of the week attached to it. Thus, if January 1 were to fall on a Sunday, then December 30 would automatically fall on a Saturday. December 31 would be Year Day and January 1 would fall on Sunday again.

In this way, all days of the year would fall on the same day of the week year after year. The same calendar would do for every year.

However this would throw off the progression of the week. December 31 might be called Year Day but to many Christians it would still be Sunday and the Lord's Day. Calling January 1 Sunday might not make it Sunday to them. In the same way, the Jewish Sabbath (Saturday) and the Mohammedan day of rest (Friday) would be upset.

In fact, many religious bodies of all types are staunchly against any calendar reform that will upset the week, so there seems very little chance of such a reform being accepted.

It has also been suggested that the year be made exactly 52 weeks long (364 days). Thus, all days of the month would fall on the same day each year. Of course, this means that each year the calendar would fall a day behind the sun (actually a day and a quarter). However, when seven such days had been collected, the calendar could be made to catch up by introducing a year with an extra week added. The year with the *intercalary week* would be 53 weeks long (371 days). In this way, the days of the week would remain untouched and Sunday would always come on Sunday.

However, this would make the years fairly uneven, some being 2% longer than others. This would displease the businessman who wants to calculate his books on years that are as much alike as possible. It would upset those holidays that are tied to the sun. Finally, it would be complicated. There would have to be five 53-week years in every 28 and these could not be simply arranged.

It looks as if there is no way out.

CHAPTER 8

Those Extra Days

Julius Caesar Takes a Hand

The Egyptians, I have said, adopted a Solar Calendar because of the extreme importance of the annual Nile flood which was tied to the sun. Apparently it took a combination of circumstances to get the Solar Calendar adopted in other countries. It needed a strong man in charge who insisted on having his way and who controlled the religious machinery as well as the government. And it needed an old calendar which had fallen into a hopeless mess.

All this had happened in Rome by 46 B.C. The Romans were, at that time, still using a Lunar Calendar with intercalary months as in the Hebrew system. (The intercalary month was named *Mercedonius,* from a Latin word for "wages," since its coming meant an extra month's pay. It was added every other year in the middle of February, and was composed of 22 or 23 days.) However, the Roman priesthood was not as conscientious about it as were the Hebrew priests. By 46 B.C., the Roman calendar was 80 days behind the Sun. The winter months were falling in the autumn, the autumn months in the summer and so on.

Meanwhile, at the head of the Roman government at the time was Julius Caesar. He was one of the men in history who knew what he wanted and never hesitated about grabbing for it. He was in control of both the Roman government and of the Roman religion. Furthermore, Caesar had just returned from Egypt where he had observed the workings of the Egyptian Solar Calendar.

Caesar saw his duty and did it without hesitation. He decreed that the year 46 B.C. was to continue for 445 days (the longest year in civilized history and called ever since "The Year of Confusion") to enable the calendar to catch up with the sun. The two extra months were called "Undecember" ("one after December") and "Duodecember" ("two after December"). The next year, 45 B.C., was to begin a new system altogether.

(Of course, the Romans did not number their years "B.C." since they had no way of knowing that the year of calendar reform was 46 years before the birth of Christ. They used another system, which I'll describe in the next chapter. We needn't worry about it now, though.)

Beginning in 45 B.C., the Roman calendar was a strictly Solar Calendar. What's more, it was one that was even better than the Egyptian one.

The Egyptian year was 365 days long, but actually, the Tropical Year (from solstice to solstice, or from equinox to equinox) is closer to $365\frac{1}{4}$ days long. This meant that every year, the Egyptian calendar fell a quarter of a day (six hours) behind the sun. Every four years, it fell a full day behind the sun.

The same thing happened to the ancient Egyptians that happens to the modern Mohammedans, except much more slowly. After 1461 years, the Egyptian calendar fell a full year behind the sun. In that time, the seasons passed completely round the calendar. (A calendar very similar to this was used by the Mayas, the South American Indians who built an interesting civilization in what is now Yucatan and Guatemala, a thousand years before the coming of Columbus.)

The astronomers knew better, of course. As long ago as about 380 B.C., the Greek astronomer, Eudoxus of Cnidus had calculated the length of the year to be 365 days and 6 hours. Long before Caesar's time, Egyptian astronomers kept their own year at a length of 365¼ days. The Egyptian people, however, those ultra-conservatives, were used to the slowly moving year and wouldn't have it interfered with. In 239 B.C. the Egyptian king, Ptolemy III, tried to get them to adjust the calendar for that quarter-day and failed.

Julius Caesar knew about that extra quarter-day, too. (He had a Greek astronomer from Alexandria, Egypt, named Sosigenes, helping him.) He decided not to fool around. As long as he was standing the Roman calendar on its head, he might as well do the job well.

So he decreed that though every ordinary year was to have 365 days, every fourth year was to have an intercalary day and come to 366 days. In this way, the year caught up with the sun again.

The 366-day year we call *Leap Year* and the extra day is *Leap Day*. These are called so for the following reason. The ordinary year is 52 weeks and 1 day long, as I said at the end of the previous chapter. A particular day of the year which falls on Sunday one year will fall on Monday the next because of that extra day.

Leap Year, however, with 366 days, is 52 weeks and 2 days long. A particular day of the year which falls on Sunday one year will fall on Tuesday the next if Leap Day falls in between. The day will have moved 2 days because of those two extra days and will have leapt, so to speak, over Monday.

This type of Solar Calendar, with a Leap Year every fourth year, is called the *Julian Calendar*, and the year is the *Julian Year* after Julius Caesar.

The Romans began their year on the Ides of March (March 15), which was nearly the time of the vernal equinox. However, the Roman consuls took office on January 1, which was thus the beginning of the political year. Julius Caesar fixed January 1 as the beginning of the year in all ways; and, by an odd coincidence, he was assassinated two years later on the demoted Ides of March.

Thirty Days Hath September

The Julian Calendar distributed the days among the months better than did the Egyptian calendar, too. The Egyptians had eleven 30-day months and one 35-day month. Caesar spread the days more evenly.

In leap years, the months had 31 days and 30 days alternately. Thus, in the full year there were six 31-day months and six 30-day months, for a total of 366 days.

In ordinary 365-day years, one of those days had to be removed. The logical thing would have been to take a day away from one of the 31-day months. That would leave seven 30-day months and five 31-day months and that would keep things as even as possible.

Actually, this was not done. It was February, one of the 30-day months that lost a day. It was left with only 29 days during ordinary years. Some suggest that the reason for this is that the Romans felt February to be an unlucky month so that the shorter it was, the better. If so, it is too bad that the Romans let foolish superstition make the months any more uneven than necessary. Any unevenness just complicates the calendar. Nor did Caesar disturb the traditional system of ides, nones and calends. That didn't stop till the time of Constantine, who introduced the week over three centuries later.

After Caesar's assassination, when his adopted nephew, Augustus Caesar, was Rome's first Emperor, there was more adjustment of the calendar because the priests mistakenly added a Leap Year every three years, instead of every four. Since the month of Quintilis had been

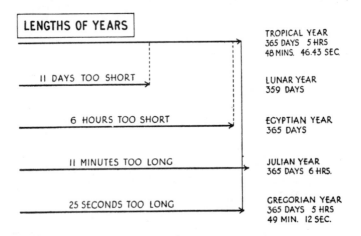

LENGTHS OF YEARS

	TROPICAL YEAR 365 DAYS 5 HRS 48 MINS. 46.43 SEC.
11 DAYS TOO SHORT	LUNAR YEAR 359 DAYS
6 HOURS TOO SHORT	EGYPTIAN YEAR 365 DAYS
11 MINUTES TOO LONG	JULIAN YEAR 365 DAYS 6 HRS.
25 SECONDS TOO LONG	GREGORIAN YEAR 365 DAYS 5 HRS 49 MIN. 12 SEC.

named Julius (July) in Julius Caesar's honor, the month of Sextilis was named Augustus (August) in the Emperor's honor, in 8 B.C.

Although it may not be true, the story is that Augustus wanted his month, which had 30 days to begin with, to have as many days as his uncle's. Therefore, another day was added to it, that day being taken from the already short-changed February, leaving it shorter than ever.

By that time, we had the arrangement that has persisted ever since, for two thousand years, as follows:

> January — 31 days
> February — 28 days (29 in Leap Year)
> March — 31 days
> April — 30 days
> May — 31 days
> June — 30 days
> July — 31 days
> August — 31 days
> September — 30 days
> October — 31 days
> November — 30 days
> December — 31 days

The superstition and pride that cut down February and built up August has permanently spoiled the alternation of 30's and 31's. That just makes it harder for people to keep the calendar straight. Perhaps that is why the jingle was invented that goes:

> *Thirty days hath September,*
> *April, June and November,*
> *All the rest have thirty-one,*
> *Excepting February alone,*
> *Which has twenty-eight days clear,*
> *And twenty-nine in each leap year.*

Still, it might have been worse. There were movements after Augustus's time to have other months named after other Emperors. None succeeded. If they had, each Emperor might have aimed for a longer month and all would have ended in a mess.

THE CLOCK WE LIVE ON

February 29 is Leap Day. People who are born on February 29 have an odd situation with regard to birthdays. Gilbert and Sullivan even wrote a comic opera, "The Pirates of Penzance," based on that situation. Yet such birthdays aren't rare. One out of every 1,461 days is a Leap Day and since as many babies are born on that day as on any other, about one out of every 1461 human beings must be born on Leap Day. That means over 100,000 Americans alone, and perhaps 2,000,000 in the world altogether.

Pope Gregory Takes a Hand

It would certainly seem that after Julius Caesar's time the Solar Calendar was in good shape. The Lunar Year fell 11 days behind the sun each year. The Egyptian Year did better and fell only 6 hours behind the sun each year. Surely the Julian Year was now even with the sun so that the matter could be forgotten?

Well, not exactly. By having 365 days a year three years out of four, and 366 days a year on the fourth year, the Julian Year averaged out to be $365\frac{1}{4}$ days long, exactly. This would be fine if the Tropical Year were actually $365\frac{1}{4}$ days long exactly. In that case, the calendar would remain even with the sun for ever.

However, the length of the year is not so conveniently even. As long ago as the second century B.C., the Greek astronomer, Hipparchus of Nicaea, realized the year was a trifle shorter than that. The Tropical Year, from winter solstice to winter solstice, according to modern computation, is 365 days 5 hours 48 minutes 45.66 seconds long. This makes it just over 11 minutes shorter than 365¼ days. Consequently, every year, the Julian Year gains on the sun by those 11 minutes. If the Julian Year were to continue indefinitely, the seasons of the year would drift through the entire year in about 46,720 years.

This might seem too long a time to worry about, but it means that in 128 years, the Julian Year gains a full day on the sun. By late medieval times, it had gained ten days on the sun since the time of Constantine in A.D. 325, when the Church had adjusted the holy days to the Julian Calendar, and the difference was very noticeable to astronomers. The vernal equinox was coming on March 11 instead of on March 21. The same advance had occurred in the other equinox and in both solstices.

This might not bother the ordinary man. It meant that planting time and harvest time came ten days earlier (according to the calendar) than it had come a thousand years back, but what of it?

However, it did bother the Church dignitaries. One of the rules for calculating Easter was that March 21, on the calendar was to be taken as the vernal equinox, regardless of the real date of the vernal equinox. This meant that Easter was being celebrated a day further into the spring each 128 years. It also meant that Christmas was being celebrated a day further into the winter each 128 years.

If this were to continue, the Church realized, then eventually, Easter would be celebrated in midsummer and Christmas in the spring. This, many Churchmen felt, must not be allowed to happen. An English scholar, Roger Bacon, who was also a monk, wrote a letter to Pope Urban IV in 1263. He thought it was time to adjust the calendar. However, any change in the calendar is difficult to put across. Three more centuries passed. In 1545, a great council of churchmen at Trent in northern Italy directed the Pope to take action in the matter. Still there was delay, but finally, in 1582, the Pope, who was then Gregory XIII, made the necessary changes.

With the advice of the German astronomer, Christopher Clavius, Pope Gregory decreed first that October 5, 1582 should be October 15, 1582. In this way, the calendar was set even with the sun again.

Then, in order to avoid the same thing happening over again in another few centuries, he decreed a change in the Leap Year system. Every fourth year was still to be Leap Year, but with a few exceptions. Years that ended in a double 0 were not to be Leap Years unless they were divisible by 400.

In the Julian Year, for instance, every century year, 1600, 1700, 1800, 1900, 2000, 2100 and so on, is a Leap Year. In the new calendar, 1600 and 2000 (which are divisible by 400) would still be Leap Years, but the years 1700, 1800, 1900 and 2100 (which are not divisible by 400) would not be Leap Years.

This new calendar is called the *Gregorian Calendar* in honor of the pope and is the calendar used by the civilized world, without further change, to this day. Every 400 years, according to the Gregorian Calendar, there are 303 ordinary years and 97 Leap Years, or 146,097 days. (In 400 years, the Julian Calendar had 300 ordinary years and 100 Leap Years for 146,100 days.)

The average length of the *Gregorian Year* is 146097/400, or 365.2425 days. In hours, minutes and seconds, this comes to 365 days 5 hours 49 minutes 12 seconds. This is still about 25 seconds longer than the Tropical Year, so the Gregorian Year gains that much a year on the sun. Although the Gregorian Year is thus not perfect, 25 seconds a year mean it won't gain a full day for some 3,400 years. (Meanwhile the Soviet government has adopted a new arrangement of Leap Years that is even more accurate than the Gregorian arrangement. For instance, 2800 will be a Leap Year on the Gregorian calendar but not on the Russian calendar, while 2900 will be a Leap Year on the Russian calendar but not on the Gregorian. The Russian calendar will go about 35,000 years before gaining a full day on the sun, since the Russian Year is only 2 seconds longer than the Tropical Year.)

Julius Caesar Hangs On

However, the Church had partly lost its chance. It should have made the reform when the discussion about it first came up a century and more before Pope Gregory's time. Then, Christendom had been united and all Western Europe would have obeyed and followed the reform.

As it was, by 1582, the Protestant Reformation was 65 years old and large parts of Europe were decidedly hostile to the Pope. They were used to the old Julian calendar and, anyway, would rather be astronomically wrong on their own than right with the Pope.

So although Italy, Spain, Portugal, Poland and France (all strongly Catholic) adopted the new calendar at once, and Hungary and parts of Germany followed soon after, other nations hesitated.

Denmark and the Protestant parts of Germany and the Netherlands adopted the Gregorian calendar in 1700, but England did not adopt it until September 2, 1752. By that time, two century years had passed. The year 1600 was divisible by 400, so it was a Leap Year by the Gregorian as well as the Julian calendar. The year 1700 was a Leap Year only by the Julian calendar. By 1752, when England changed, the Julian calendar was 11 days ahead of the sun and 11 days had to be dropped.

England also seized the opportunity to change the

beginning of the year from March 25 to January 1. The old beginning still may linger with us in "April Fool's Day," because some think that this originated as the final day of a week-long celebration of the new year.

There were riots in England at that. Many people foolishly thought that their lives had been shortened and gathered in crowds before the halls of Parliament, crying, "Give us back our eleven days." Apparently, they did not realize that you can call a day or a year anything you want without affecting your age. Everyone could agree right now to call this year 1950 and nobody would be one second younger for that. Or we could call it 2000 and nobody would be older.

Anyway, for many years afterwards, the people of England kept both calendars, even though only the Gregorian Calendar was official. They would date a letter March 5, 1783 O.S. (meaning *Old Style*; that is, according to the Julian Calendar) or March 16, 1783 N.S. (meaning *New Style*; that is, according to the Gregorian Calendar). Both these dates refer to the same day.

To Americans, all this is important. In 1752, the colonies had not yet achieved their independence. British laws held for them and therefore the calendar was changed from Julian to Gregorian in 1752 in the colonies also.

This means that if you would care to make a bet with anyone, you can very safely bet that George Washington was not born on February 22, despite the fact that that is Washington's birthday on the Calendar. Washington, you see, was born in the year 1732, at which time the official calendar in his native Virginia, as in all other British dominions, was the Julian Calendar. The day on which George Washington was born was, therefore, officially February 11, 1732.

THOSE EXTRA DAYS

After Virginia switched to the Gregorian Calendar in 1752, Washington very sensibly switched his birthday, too, from February 11 to February 22. In this way he shifted the calendar date but kept the anniversary of the actual day—and himself the mathematically correct age.

Great Britain was by no means the last European nation to adopt the Gregorian Calendar. The Orthodox Catholic Church, to which most people in East Europe and the Balkans belong, was even more stubborn than the western Protestant nations and for that matter, more stubborn than some non-European nations. The Chinese under their Empire used a lunar calendar with a 19-year cycle something like the Babylonian calendar. With the establishment of the Chinese Republic in 1911, however, the Gregorian Calendar was adopted. It wasn't until after World War I, however, that the governments of countries like Russia and Greece adopted the Gregorian calendar.

By that time, the years 1800 and 1900 had passed. Both of them were Leap Years according to the Julian Calendar, but not according to the Gregorian Calendar. So the Julian Calendar is now 13 days ahead of the Gregorian and 13 days had to be dropped.

Yet the Greek Orthodox Church itself still refuses to accept the Gregorian Calendar to this day. Thus, the various Orthodox churches in the United States, for instance, celebrate Christmas on December 25 O.S., which is January 7, according to our calendar.

The year 2000 will be a Leap Year in both calendars, so the 13-day discrepancy will grow no worse until 2100. Then there will a Leap Year in the Julian Calendar and not in the Gregorian, so that the discrepancy will be 14 days. The Orthodox Christmas will then be on January 8.

Perhaps by then the Orthodox Church will have given in but they've held out this long and they may hold out centuries longer.

The Revolutionaries Take a Hand

The one serious attempt to alter the modern calendar since the time of Pope Gregory XIII, did not tamper with the length of the year, but it did reorganize everything else.

This was during the French Revolution that began in 1789. The Revolutionaries were breaking with tradition. They had scrapped France's old systems of measurements, for instance, and invented a new one based on the number ten. This was a great success. It is the *metric system* and is today used not only by France but by all the civilized world except the English-speaking countries.

They were less successful in reorganizing the calendar. In 1792, the Revolutionaries established a year which began at just about the autumnal equinox (which is about the time the Hebrew Year starts). September 22, 1792, was the day that the monarchy was abolished and the First French Republic was proclaimed. The coincidence of having this fall so close to the autumnal equinox was very convenient.

The individual months, then, were given new names (invented by a minor French poet, named Fabre d'Eglantine) after the sort of weather those months might be expected to show:

September 22 — October 21; Vendémiare (vintage)
October 22 — November 20; Brumaire (fog)
November 21 — December 20; Frimaire (sleet)
December 21 — January 19; Nivôse (snow)
January 20 — February 18; Pluviôse (rain)
February 19 — March 20; Ventôse (wind)

THOSE EXTRA DAYS

March 21 — April 19; Germinal (seed)
April 20 — May 19; Floréal (flower)
May 20 — June 18; Prairial (pasture)
June 19 — July 18; Messidor (harvest)
July 19 — August 17; Thermidor (heat)
August 18 — September 16; Fructidor (fruit)

Each month has 30 days, coming to 360 days altogether. From September 17 to 21 inclusive are five holidays that belong to no month. That brings the total number of days to 365 (and this is very much like the Egyptian calendar). There would be six holidays on Leap Year and Leap Years would follow the Gregorian system.

What's more, the week was abolished. Each month was divided into three groups of ten days each, called decades, and this was also similar to the Egyptian system. The days of the decade were numbered in Latin: Primidi, Duodi (First Day, Second Day), and so on.

The calendar seems very logical; the French being noted for their logic. The months are equal and fit in exactly with the seasons. The first three (autumn) have names that end in "-aire," the second three (winter) have names that end in "-ôse," whilst the third three (spring) have names that end in "-al" and the fourth three (summer) have names that end in "-idor."

Furthermore, it seems sensible to name months after weather conditions. We ourselves talk about March winds, April showers and May flowers.

But there were several catches. Even if other European countries (which were at war with France at the time) were willing to accept a French calendar and use French words for the days and months, the Revolutionary Calendar broke up the succession of Sundays. That could not be accepted.

Then, too, what a ridiculous calendar it would have been for the rest of the world. After all, weather conditions are different in various regions. In the southern hemisphere the seasons are just the opposite of those in the northern hemisphere. In Argentina, Thermidor (heat) would come in midwinter, and Nivôse (snow) in midsummer. Arabia would wonder at a month named after rain and the Congo would wonder why a month should be named after sleet.

No, the French Revolutionary calendar was simply not a good idea. So it wasn't adopted outside France. And even in France it only held good for a little over thirteen years and was then abandoned.

About the only thing left of the French Revolutionary calendar is that some of the historical events of the time are often referred to by the French date on which it occurred. For instance, the Reign of Terror ended on July 27, 1794, when Robespierre (the Revolutionary dictator) and his followers were arrested and held for execution. This was Thermidor 9 and the event is sometimes spoken of as the "Revolution of Thermidor." The people who carried it through called themselves "Thermidorians" for a while after that.

Later, Napoleon seized power on November 9, 1799. This was Brumaire 18, and the event is always spoken of as the "coup d'état of Brumaire."

Actually, a logical way to improve on the names of the months is simply to number them as we number the days of the month. We do this now when we write dates in short form. August 12, for instance, may be written 8/12. There is one possibility of confusion here. Some might take it to mean the "8th of December." However, if everyone would agree to write the number of the month first (or the number of the day first) it could work.

THOSE EXTRA DAYS

Modern calendar reform is concentrating on making the four quarters of the year equal. There is a movement in favor of a *World Calendar,* so called, in which the months have 31, 30, 30, 31, 30, 30, 31, 30, 30, 31, 30, and 30 days. Each three-month quarter year has 91 days and the same date comes on the same day of the week each year.

The total number of days in such a year would be 364 so a "Year Day" can be added as the 365th. It would have no weekday attached. In Leap Years, a "Leap Day" with no weekday attached would be added at the end of June.

Earlier there had been a move in favor of a 13-month year, the *International Fixed Calendar,* each with 28 days and all exactly alike. The thirteenth month was to be called "Sol" and was to come between June and July. The trouble with that notion, however, is that 13 months cannot be divided evenly in any way, which is inconvenient. For this reason, the 13-month notion is about abandoned.

CHAPTER 9

Counting the Years

Year-Identification

Once the year is established—any kind of year, a Lunar Year or a Gregorian Year—it becomes desirable to tell the different years apart.

To begin with, probably the only way of doing that was to make mention of some notable event that had happened in that year. We ourselves do it in conversation with family or friends. We say, "That was the year Cousin Sue came to visit," or "Back in the year when I was a high-school senior," and so on.

To identify the year generally, you need a more general reminder. For instance, in New York, 1888 is the Year of the Blizzard; and 1947 is the Year of the Big Snow. In New England, 1934 is the Year of the Freeze, 1938 the Year of the Hurricane and 1955 the Year of the Flood. For the nation as a whole, 1941 is the Year of Pearl Harbor, and 1929 is the Year of the Stock Market Crash.

One can fill in the less dramatic years by numbering them from the important ones. You might say: "It was three years after the Stock Market Crash" or "It was just a year before Pearl Harbor."

In ancient times, it was customary to use a somewhat more regular system by referring to the reigns of kings. In the Bible, for instance, the length of the reign of each king of Israel and Judah is carefully noted. This was probably because events were dated in accordance with those reigns. Something was said to take place, for instance, "in the 3rd year of Jehoshaphat" or "in the 22nd year of Manasseh."

Records kept this way can be useful to scribes and others who spend their time working with court annals. Ordinary people might find matters difficult. Suppose we used such a system here in America. Could you tell, quickly, when the second year of Garfield was, or the third year of Hayes ? Could you even tell which came first ?

This constant beginning over again each time a new king came into power finally passed out of the picture (though it is still used as a matter of form on official papers in some nations which are monarchies).

It was more convenient to pick some one year and count all other years from that without ever starting over again. In this way, a *chronological era* is established.

A Variety of Eras

The Greeks were forced to establish a chronological era quite early in the game. They were broken up into a large number of independent cities, mostly republican. Each counted years by its own officials, often by elected officials who served for only one year. Thus, Athens listed its years as "the year when so-and-so was archon." (The archon was the Athenian chief magistrate.) This might be convenient for officials in Athens but what good was it to other cities ?

In finding a system that would suit everybody, the Greeks (who considered themselves the only truly civilized peoples and didn't bother with "barbarians") turned to the one event which was celebrated by all Greeks alike. This was the famous Olympic Games.

These games were celebrated every four years, so a period of four years was therefore called an *Olympiad*. When a Greek of any city said that something had happened in the second year of the 92nd Olympiad, Greeks of all other cities understood him. In this way, the *Era of the Olympiads* was established.

Historians have checked back on the Era of Olympiads, comparing the date of some event given in that system by historians of those times, with the date of the same event given by other historians of the time who used a different system. That ties up those two systems. The second system is tied to a third system in the same way. Finally, we can combine some system or other with the one we use. In this way, we can work back again to the Olympiads and find what the dates mean in our system. (Any ancient eclipse that is given even an approximate date in some local system is a stroke of great good fortune. We can calculate back astronomically and get the exact day of that eclipse by our own system.)

Working in this fashion, it turns out that the First Olympiad (according to Greek records) began in 776 B.C. by our system of numbering years. Therefore, the battle of Marathon (490 B.C.) was fought in the 3rd year of the 71st Olympiad. Alexander the Great died (323 B.C.) in the 2nd year of the 113th Olympiad.

If we want to extend the Era of the Olympiads to our own day, Pearl Harbor was attacked in the 2nd year of the 679th Olympiad, and 1960 begins the 684th Olympiad.

The main difficulty with the Era of the Olympiads is the four-year interval. It is simpler to number the years one by one in steady progression. For this reason other systems were established, particularly after the conquest of western Asia by Alexander the Great. People of Greek culture were

BEGINNING OF THE ERAS

Name of Era	Alternate Names (if any)	Year of Christian Era It Began
Byzantine Era	Mundane Era of Constantinople	5508 B.C.
Mundane Era of Alexandria		5500
Mundane Era of Antioch		5490
Julian Day 1		4713
Christian Mundane Era		4004
Jewish Mundane Era		3760
Mayan Era		3641
Hindu Era		3012
Chinese Era		2277
Era of Abraham		2016
Era of the Olympiads		776
Roman Era	Era of Varro	753
Era of Nabonasser		747
Japanese Era		660
Buddhist Era		543
Seleucid Era	Syrian Era, Macedonian Era, Syro-Macedonian Era	312
Era of the Maccabees		166
Julian Era		45
Spanish Era	Era of the Caesars	38
Actian Era		32
Augustan Era		27
Christian Era	Dionysian Era, Common Era	1 A.D.
Diocletian Era	Era of the Martyrs	284
Armenian Era		552
Mohammedan Era		622
Persian Era		632
Republican Era		1792

left ruling large populations of non-Greeks. These populations weren't used to the Olympiad system and felt no traditional respect for it. For instance, the Greek astronomers at Alexandria dated their years from the time when Nabonasser became King of Babylon. This *Era* of *Nabonasser* begins in 747 B.C., and it was useful to the astronomers because it tied in their observations with those made centuries earlier by the Babylonians.

Then in the Asiatic regions of what was left of Alexander's Empire after his death a new chronological era was established. These regions belonged to the Seleucid Empire, which was called that because its first ruler was one of Alexander's generals named Seleucus Nicator. In 312 B. C. Seleucus Nicator won the battle of Gaza, captured Babylon, and officially established his rule. So this was considered the year 1 of the new era.

The new era was called variously the Syrian Era, the Macedonian Era, the Syro-Macedonian Era, and the Greek Era, but it is most frequently called the *Seleucid Era*. The year 1960, for instance, is 2272 of the Seleucid Era.

The Seleucid Era was used in Western Asia long after the Seleucid Empire came to an end in 64 B.C. (258 of the Seleucid Era). Once a society has started numbering its years in a certain way, it is very inconvenient to change the numbering system, since that complicates all previous records.

For instance, the Jews, who lived under the rule of the Seleucid kings for a number of years, won their independence in 142 B.C. or 180 of the Seleucid Era. They tried to establish a new era then, beginning with the first year in 166 B.C. when, under Judas Maccabeus, they first revolted against the Seleucid kings. Thus, 180 of the Seleucid Era was also 14 of the *Era of the Maccabees*.

However, the Jews found it too inconvenient to switch

eras and for business purposes kept up the Seleucid Era for a long time even after they were scattered over the Roman Empire. In fact, that is what makes the Seleucid Era so important since through the Jews one can compare it with many local eras and other methods of keeping track of the years. In this way, dates can be systematized.

From the Beginning of the City

In ancient times, though, the most important chronological eras were those developed in Rome. For a space of 600 years in actuality (and for additional centuries in theory), Rome ruled all the civilized European world, and its system was used everywhere.

The Romans had their specialized eras, too. For instance, there is the *Julian Era*, which begins with the reform of the calendar by Julius Caesar. Year 1 of the Julian Era is therefore 45 B.C. This has something to recommend it, since the calendar ever since (at least in the western world) has been essentially the same. Before that, the calendars followed different systems and some were badly confused.

Less reasonable are various eras that were begun in order to flatter Julius Caesar's successor, Augustus Caesar. The *Spanish Era*, for instance, begins in 38 B.C. when Augustus (then called simply Octavian Caesar) conquered Spain and became an important man in the Roman world. This, also called the *Era of the Caesars,* was actually used to some extent in Southwest Europe until almost 1400. The *Actian Era* begins in 32 B.C. when Augustus defeated Mark Antony at the sea-battle of Actium, and became the dictator of the Roman world. Finally, the *Augustan Era* begins in 27 B.C., when Octavian was awarded the title of Augustus.

All these eras were used here and there, but none

really took hold. A more successful system was established much later in honor of Diocletian, one of the later Roman Emperors. This *Diocletian Era* starts in A.D. 284 when Diocletian was first proclaimed Emperor. (It is also called the *Era of the Martyrs,* because the last important Roman persecution of Christianity took place in his reign.) Although it had no better luck in Rome than the other eras, it is actually still used today among the Coptic Christians of Egypt and Ethiopia.

The era that was really used throughout later Roman history, and even for a number of centuries after the fall of Rome, was the *Roman Era*, based on the date of the founding of the city of Rome. This is sometimes called the *Era of Varro* because the Roman historian, Marcus Terentius Varro, was the one who traced back the early records and decided that Rome was founded on a date that corresponds to our own 753 B.C.

The Roman writers regularly used the abbreviation A.U.C. in number dates in the Roman Era. This stands for "Anno Urbis Conditae" meaning "the year of the founding of the city." Thus, the assassination of Julius Caesar (44 B.C.) took place in 709 A.U.C.

A similar notion in the Orient led to the *Japanese Era,* which dates from 660 B.C., the date when the legendary first emperor, Jimmu, began to reign, while the *Chinese Era* dates from 2277 B.C., when the legendary first emperor, Yao, began his reign. The Mayans of Central America on the other side of the world counted their years from 3641 B. C. (*Mayan Era.*)

From the Beginning of the World

The Roman Era gradually became less popular after the

rise of Christianity. Christian writers were naturally anxious to show that the Biblical records extended further back than did the pagan records of Greece and Rome. For that reason, they sometimes counted from the time of the birth of the patriarch, Abraham.

An early Church historian, Eusebius of Caesarea, using Biblical records and outside traditions, decided this had taken place 1263 years before the founding of Rome. That makes it 2016 B.C. according to our present system.

Thus, the abdication of the last West Roman Emperor (usually referred to as the "Fall of Rome"), which took place in 1229 A.U.C. (or 476 A.D.), occurred in the year 2492 of the *Era of Abraham*. The year 1964 would be the year 3980 of this Era. (The Hindus had a similar idea and the *Hindu Era* starts at 3012 B.C. which was the date they set for the Deluge.)

However, the Jews and Christians both had an even more far-reaching idea. Any ordinary era has the problem of dating events that take place before the beginning of the era. We ourselves have this problem.

This wasn't much of a bother for the Greeks, who didn't care much about dating anything before the first Olympic Games (except for the Trojan War). Similarly, the Romans didn't care much about dating events before the founding of Rome (except for the Trojan War). Such questions did, however, bother the Jews and Christians who were seriously interested in events all the way back to the Creation.

What they tried to do, then, was to figure out how many years back the date of the Creation must have been. In so doing, a *Mundane Era* could be established. ("Mundane" comes from a Latin word meaning "world" so a "Mundane Era" was an "era of the world.") The years could be counted from the very first year there was and no one would have to worry about years before the era began.

The best-known such era that is still in existence is the *Jewish Mundane Era*, used from the 10th Century down to this day in counting the years in the Jewish Calendar. The Jewish biblical experts calculated that Creation had taken place in 3760 B.C. September,1964, is therefore the beginning cf the Jewish year 5725.

Various Christian calculators came up with different results. About 1650, Archbishop Ussher (an Irish-born bishop of the Anglican Church), calculated the date of the Creation as 4004 B.C. (Christian Mundane Era). This is the most familiar date to us and is given in the margins of many editions of the Bible. However, earlier calculations had placed it variously at 5490 B.C. (the *Mundane Era of Antioch*), 5500 B.C. (the *Mundane Era of Alexandria*) and 5508 B.C.

This last one, the *Mundane Era of Constantinople,* was in use for a number of centuries in the Eastern Roman Empire (also called the Byzantine Empire) which had its capital at Constantinople. It is therefore also called the *Byzantine Era.* It was used in Russia until the time of Peter the Great. In 1700, he decreed that Russia was to adopt the Julian Calendar, probably in imitation of England, a nation he greatly admired. (However, when England abandoned the Julian Calendar for the Gregorian a half-century later, Peter was dead and Russia did not go along.) The Byzantine Era is still used in some of the Orthodox churches. The year 1964 is 7472 of the Byzantine Era.

The One That Won

All these eras, however, even the mundane eras, were replaced by one based on the event which Christians consider the most important in history, the birth of Christ. The Bible does not give the exact day of the birth or even the exact year. It simply says: "And it came to pass in those days, that there went out a decree from Caesar Augustus that all the world should be taxed, and this taxing was first made when Cyrenius was governor of Syria."

This dates it by the local overlord of the time, which was common enough, but leaves matters a little doubtful. Augustus is known to have reigned from 742 A.U.C. to 787 A.U.C. so the birth of Christ must have taken place between those two limits. Finding the years when Cyrenius was governor of Syria would cut it down further but this was harder to do.

About 535 A.D. a scholar named Dionysius Exiguus produced arguments to show that the birth of Christ must have taken place in 753 A.U.C. There began a movement, therefore, to date events from that year. Oddly enough, it took quite a time for this movement to win out, despite the importance of the event and the fact that the Europeans of the day were devout Christians. It just proves again that, of all things, the calendar is the hardest to tamper with.

This new *Christian Era* (also called the *Dionysian Era*, sometimes, after Dionysius Exiguus) was adopted first by the Church itself in Rome. The first important civilian ruler to adopt the new system was probably Charlemagne in the late 700's.

Charlemagne was a strong ruler, one of the few who, like Julius Caesar, could even dominate the calendar. When he followed the new system that settled things. First his Empire (which included modern France and Germany, plus most of Italy) followed suit and, eventually, everyone else.

Dates before the birth of Christ are now labeled *B.C.*

(Before Christ). Thus, Socrates was executed in 390 B.C. Dates after the birth of Christ are now labelled *A.D.* (an abbreviation for "Anno Domini" meaning "the year of the Lord"). Thus, Pearl Harbor was bombed in 1941 A.D.

This era is now used among many peoples who are not Christian in religion and it is just about world-wide. Even those who are faithful to their own eras, particularly in connection with their religion, use the Christian Era also, if only for business purposes or international dealings.

English-speaking non-Christians have a tendency sometimes to call the era the *Common Era,* to avoid offending their own beliefs. They may abbreviate dates as 1941 C.E. and 390 B.C.E. ("Before the Common Era").

There is also a tendency sometimes to do away with abbreviations altogether and simply date the B.C. years with a minus sign. Thus, the Battle of Zama in which Rome finally defeated Hannibal, can be said to have been fought in the year –202.

One thing to remember in connection with our modern method of numbering the years is that the year before 1 A.D. is 1 B.C. There is no year labeled 0.

Another even odder matter in connection with the Christian Era is that Dionysius Exiguus apparently picked the wrong year for the birth of Christ. According to the Gospel of St. Matthew, Herod "the Great" was still alive at the time of Christ's birth. It is now well established that Herod died in 749 A.U.C., four years before the year picked by Dionysius to begin the Christian Era. Therefore Christ could not have been born later than 4 B.C. and some people think it may even have been 7 B.C. or earlier.

It seems odd to say that Christ was born 4 B.C., that is, four years before his own birth, but it is too late to change things and move the entire era back four years. (It would convert 1960 to 1964, for instance.) The confusion would be unbelievable. So matters stand as they are, and Christ's birth is generally given in history books as 4 B.C.

Later Variations

Since the establishment of the Christian Era, a few new eras have been started among Christians. The *Armenian Era* dates from 552 A.D. when the Armenian church became independent of control by Constantinople. However, only one new era has arisen that is used over a wide area of the Earth's surface. That is the *Mohammedan Era.*

The Mohammedan era counts the years from 622 A.D., which is the date of the "Hegira," or the flight of Mohammed from Mecca to Medina. The inhabitants of Medina followed Mohammed upon his arrival and supplied him with the first body of fighting men dedicated to his teachings. That date is therefore taken as the time when the religion was founded. The Mohammedan year is referred to in the Western world by the initials A. H. This stands for "Anno Hegirae" or "the year of the Hegira."

The unusual point about the Mohammedan era is that it consists of Lunar Years of 354 days each. Of all the eras I've mentioned, this is the only one which does not match every other era, year for year. For instance, since the Roman Era started in 753 B.C. any year of the Christian Era can be changed over into the Roman Era by adding 753. (This is true of the other eras except for difficulties arising from the fact that the first day of the year might not be the same in the two eras. In that case, a simple addition or subtraction may throw you off by one year. Some of my own figures in this chapter may be off by one year for that reason.)

The Mohammedan Era, however, cannot be changed into any other of the well-known eras by simple addition or subtraction.

Between the time of 622 A.D. and 1959 A.D., 1337 Solar years of about 365·2425 days (the Gregorian system, remember) have passed. The total number of days is therefore 488,093½. The number of Lunar Years in that number of days is almost 1379. In the interval, you see, the Mohammedan calendar has gained almost 42 years on the Gregorian calendar and that amounts to one year every 33 years, as I have already pointed out. For that reason, although 1959 was 1337 years since the Hegira, it was still 1379 A.H. The Mohammedan year will continue gaining on the Gregorian Year and will catch up in about twenty thousand years. The year 20874 A.D. will also be 20874 A.H.

The *Persian Era* begins in 632 A.D. (10 A.H.), when the last Persian king of pre-Mohammedan times was conquered by the Arabs. Some Persians escaped to India and kept their old fire-worshipping religion. It is these "Parsees" who still use the Persian Era.

Nations often have private nationalistic ways of numbering the years. For instance, American public documents often date something as happening in such and such a year of the independence of the United States. Thus, July 4, 1959 begins the 183rd year of this independence. It is not intended to be an era, though. It's just a bit of pride.

In the same way the followers of Mussolini, in Italy, did that sort of thing. Mussolini and his Fascisti came into power on October 28, 1922 and they liked to date years in Roman numerals from that point. They didn't consider it a new era, either, and made no attempt to replace the

Christian Era. However, they were more ostentatious about their year-numbers than the United States is. After the year XX of the "Fascist Era" Mussolini was so unpopular in Italy that he was only kept in power with German help, and in the year XXII he was executed, and that ended it.

The only serious attempt to replace the Christian Era was made by the French Revolutionaries, whose calendar I have already discussed. They began the years with the establishment of the Republic on September 22, 1792. That was the Year I of the *Republican Era*. (They also used Roman numerals.)

This was even more foolish of the Revolutionaries than the names they chose for months. To start the year I in 1792 meant all the years before 1792 would have to be changed into negative years running backward. All the history books would have to be changed. Furthermore, it would be an encouragement for every new ruler or princeling or president to start a new era in his own honor, as was being done after the time of Alexander the Great.

It was a terrible idea and, of course, it didn't last. It was abolished in the Year XIV of the Republican Era, so it didn't do even as well as Mussolini's system.

The only thing left of the Republican Era is the dating of several of the events in France of that period. People still speak of the Constitution of the Year III, for instance, and the Constitution of the Year VIII.

CHAPTER 10

Longer than a Year

Centuries and Millennia

The average man has never seriously felt the need of any larger unit of time than a year. There are terms for longer periods of time, but we could do without them if we wished and never miss them.

For instance, an Olympiad is a four-year interval. I've already discussed that. The Romans took a census every five years and called that period a *lustrum*. (The last lustrum was in 74 A.D.) Under the Roman Emperor Diocletian a system of taxation was started where assessments were revised every fifteen years. Such a fifteen-year period was called an *indiction*. The medieval church continued it and after 1200 counted them from the birth of Christ instead of from the time of Diocletian. The year 1964 began the 133rd indiction.

A more common multi-year interval and one that is still used quite frequently is the *decade*, from the Latin word for "ten," referring to a ten-year interval. The American census is carried out every ten years, which may help keep it popular in the United States. Ten years are often lumped together in common expressions such as "The Gay Nineties" or "The Roaring Twenties" which may also help to keep decades popular.

For a space of years greater than ten, there is the rather vague term, *generation*. This refers to the average length of time it takes a group of men to pass from birth to parenthood. No definite number of years is involved, but most frequently, a generation is taken to be about 33 years. In other words, there would be three generations every hundred years.

And then we have the most common terms of all: *century*, for the space of a hundred years; and, somewhat less used, *millennium* for a thousand years. These words are derived from Latin words for "hundred" and "thousand."

Very frequent mention is made of our own time as the twentieth century, meaning, naturally, the twentieth century after the birth of Christ. The first century composed the years 1 A.D. to 100 A.D., the second century, the years from 101 A.D. to 200 A.D., the third century from 201 A.D. to 300 A.D., and so on.

As you see, the number of the century is always 1 greater than the number you get after dropping the last two numbers of the year. Thus, the year 576 is part of the 6th century. In the same way, 1628 is in the 17th century, 1842 is in the 19th century and 1959 is in the 20th century.

One confusion concerns the years that end in double zero. Since the number of the century is worked out in the manner I've just explained, it is natural to suppose that 1900 is the first year of the 20th century. However, it isn't.

Remember that the 1st century had to be from 1 to 100 A.D. to include a hundred years. (1 to 99 A.D. would be only 99 years.) Therefore the 2nd century had to start at 101 A.D. and to include a hundred years it would have to end on December 31, 200 A.D. The 3rd century would start at 201 A.D. and so on. Working it forward, the 20th century started in 1901 A.D. and January 1, 1901 was the first day of the 20th century.

In the same way millennia are numbered by adding 1 to the number resulting when the last three numbers of the year are dropped. The 1st Millennium A.D. ran from 1 to 1000 A.D. We are now toward the end of the 2nd Millennium, which will close with the year 2000.

The 3rd Millennium (and the 21st century) will start on January 1, 2001, and not in 2000.

There is a theory among some Christian sects that Christ will return some day and rule for a thousand years in perfect justice before the Judgement Day and final end of the world. For this reason, the term "millennium" is sometimes used to refer to a vague future time of perfection.

There are vague terms for periods of indefinite length coming to much more than a thousand years, such as *age* or *eon*. The Egyptians, however, had a name for a definite length of time longer than a millennium.

Remember that the Egyptian year was 365 days rather than $365\frac{1}{4}$. This meant that at the end of each Egyptian year, the stars in heaven were not in exactly the same position as at the end of the previous year. The Egyptians paid particular attention to the brightest star in the heavens in this connection. That star is Sirius, which the Egyptians called Sothis.

At the beginning of one year, Sirius might rise exactly with the sun. When a star rises with the sun, that is spoken of as that star's *heliacal rising,* "helios" being the Greek name for the sun. At the time of a star's heliacal rising, it is on the same meridian as the sun. However, at the beginning of the next Egyptian year it would be on a meridian $\frac{1}{4}°$ to the east (because of the missing $\frac{1}{4}$ day of the Egyptian year). At the beginning of the next

156

year, it would be ½° to the east and so on. It would take 1461 years for the heliacal rising of Sirius to come once again at the beginning of the year, because 1461 Egyptian years is just about equal to 1460 tropical years.

This period of 1461 years the Egyptians called the *Sothic Cycle.*

The Pattern of Eclipses

However, all these periods of longer than one year are based on the year itself. They represent just so many years taken arbitrarily. Even the Sothic Cycle wouldn't exist if the Egyptian year weren't a bit wrong.

Is there any phenomenon in the heavens like day and night, or like the changing phases of the moon, or like the drift of the sun among the stars that would give rise to an entirely new unit that is longer than the year? The answer is yes. Such longer units are not useful, particularly, to ordinary folk, but they are there.

I have already explained that eclipses of the sun occur when the sun and the moon are near the nodes (that is, those points where their lines of apparent motion intersect on the Celestial Globe).

This happens at odd times and with slight variations in actual position. Consequently, different types of eclipses (total, almost total, partial, slight—of either the sun or the moon) occur. The time and place and kind of eclipse that takes place can be predicted with certainty by astronomers who have studied the apparent motions of sun and moon. In the course of 18 years and $11\frac{1}{3}$ days, about 29 Lunar Eclipses and 41 Solar Eclipses take place in a particular pattern.

Then, after that period of 18 years and $11\frac{1}{3}$ days, the sun and moon are at the same positions with respect to the nodes they were originally, and the whole cycle starts over again. Once the eclipses are predicted for one such length of time, the predictions will hold almost true for the next such length. They don't hold exactly true because there are certain unevennesses in the moon's motion that slowly throws the cycle off.)

The Babylonians discovered this cycle about 550 B.C. and called it the *Saros*. An Athenian astronomer, named Meton, used this about a century later to adjust the lunar calendar to the sun, and that system of adjustment is called the *Metonic Cycle*.

Although astronomers are satisfied with this cycle of eclipses, the ordinary observer on Earth would not be. Because of the $\frac{1}{3}$ day included in the Saros, the Earth has had time to spin $\frac{1}{3}$ of the way around. In other words, suppose an eclipse has occurred in New York. You would wait for the next cycle of eclipses in order to see a similar one. You wait and 18 years and 11 days pass (or 10 days, if there happen to be five Leap Years in the interval instead of four). Then you have to wait another $\frac{1}{3}$ of a day, or 8 hours, and in that time the Earth spins $\frac{1}{3}$ of the way around and somebody on Wake Island or New Caledonia sees it. Fortunately, an eclipse of the Moon can be seen all over the world so it turns up in each Saros period. That's how the Saros period was first discovered.

However, three Saros periods come out to 54 years and 32 days (or 31 if the Leap Years are thirteen in number instead of twelve) almost exactly. Consequently, if an eclipse is seen from a certain spot on Earth, another of the same sort will be seen from the same spot 54 years and 31 days later. Here is an astronomical phenomenon that repeats at intervals of just over half a century a kind of "triple-Saros."

The Wobbling of the Earth

But this is nothing compared to something else that is visible in the heavens and that comes about in this way.

The Earth is not a perfect sphere. It bulges very slightly about the middle. The diameter of the Earth at the equator is 26 miles more than the diameter through the poles. This isn't much in a total diameter of over 7,900 miles, but it does mean that the Earth behaves as though it were a perfect sphere with a rocky shell some 13 miles thick (at its thickest) smoothly plastered about the Equator.

The moon is usually a bit above or below the Equator. If the Earth were a perfect sphere that wouldn't matter. But the *equatorial bulge* is present, and the moon's gravity pulls at it. As a result of this pull at the bulge, the Earth wobbles like a top, but very slowly.

This wobbling causes the axis of the Earth to shift. The direction in which it is pointing makes a full circle in 25,800 years. This period of circling was first determined by the Greek astronomer, Hipparchus, about 130 B.C. Although this is a long time, the effects have shown up since the time of ancient Greece.

Remember that the positions of the equinoxes and the solstices depend on the fact that the axis is tipped. If it were always tipped in exactly the same direction, the position of the sun among the stars at equinoxes and solstices would never vary. However, the fact that the axis shifts as a result of the wobble of the Earth, means that both equinoxes and both solstices occur 50 seconds of arc farther west each year than the year before.

Because the equinox precedes itself each year, so to speak, this motion is termed the *precession of the equinoxes*. In ancient Egypt, the vernal equinox occurred when the Sun was in the constellation Taurus (the Bull). In Greek and Roman times, it occurred when the sun was in Aries (the Ram), which precedes Taurus in the zodiac. Now the sun is in Pisces (the Fish) at the vernal equinox. Every 2,150 years, the procession carries the sun and the sign of the zodiac into a new constellation.

This, however, does not affect the calendar. The Gregorian year is based on the tropical year. This is measured from solstice to solstice or equinox to equinox and takes into account the precession of equinoxes.

The year which measures the interval of time between moments when the line connecting Earth and sun is pointed at the same star (whatever the position of the axis) is the *sidereal year*. This is 365 days 6 hours 9 minutes 9·5 seconds, or 20 minutes longer than the tropical year. However, the sidereal year, like the sidereal day and the sidereal month, is only of interest to astronomers. It is not used in time-measurement in the western world, although the Hindus used it. They also used a number of eras of which the best-known is the *Buddhist Era,* which begins in 543 B.C., the legendary date of Buddha's death.

The effect of the precession of the equinoxes shows itself in the stars. It takes 25,800 years for the position of the vernal equinox to make a complete circuit of the skies. Each constellation of the Zodiac takes up $\frac{1}{12}$ of this circuit. It takes the equinox, therefore, about 2,150 years to move from the center of one constellation to that of the next.

This is just about the time that has elapsed since the Greek astronomers were working out the details of the Celestial Globe, and the differences are quite plain. Then, the vernal equinox lay in Aries the Ram, but now it is in Pisces the Fishes.

Nowadays when the sun is over the Tropic of Cancer, it is no longer in the constellation of Cancer the Crab, but in Gemini the Twins. And when it is over the Tropic of Capricorn, it is not in the constellation of Capricorn the Goat, but of Sagittarius the Archer. And the autumnal equinox is no longer in Libra the Scale, but in Virgo the Maiden.

What's more, as the Earth wobbles, the North and South Poles point to the stars in changing directions. Right now, the North Pole happens to be pointing nearly at the Pole Star. In fact for the last couple of thousand years, it has been pointing closer and closer to the Pole Star. It will reach its closest point of approach in 2095 and then it will begin to move away from it so that in a few thousand more years there will be no particularly bright star near the Celestial North Pole. Thirteen thousand years from now, the star, Vega, third brightest in the sky, will be the pole star.

After 25,800 years, the solstices and equinoxes have completed their circle and are back in the constellations from which they started. The Celestial Poles have completed their circles too, and are back where they started. This period of time is sometimes called the *Great Year*.

Back to the Day

Needless to say, all these different months and years and cycles that I have been describing in this book have made the life of the astronomer more difficult. Perhaps the moment of greatest difficulty and annoyance was when the Gregorian year was just being introduced and the Julian year was fighting hard for survival. An Italian scholar, Joseph Justus Scaliger, grew impatient and considered that after all, everything depended upon the day.

The month, you see, is only an expression of the number of days in one cycle of Moon phases. The year is only an expression of the number of days in one circle of the sun about the celestial sphere. People might argue about months and years but no one ever argued about days. A day was a day.

So Scaliger suggested that astronomers simply number each day and be done with it. (This is impractical for ordinary folk, but the convenience for astronomers would make the extra trouble worth it. Other people could then argue months and years till they were blue in the face, but astronomers need not mind. They could follow heavenly motions by the day without ever worrying about what day of the year it was or what era the year was being counted in.)

The only difficulty was to find a particular day that would do as Day 1. Naturally, such a day should be far enough in the past so that astronomers would not be very likely to run into negative day numbers in keeping their records, in calculating backward for eclipses and so on. Nor should it be too far back lest the number of modern days be needlessly large.

What Scaliger did was to take what was called the *Julian Cycle*, which consisted of 7,980 Julian years. In such a cycle there are an even number of Lunar Months, and Saros cycles, and indictions and a few other things. In other words, a number of varieties of time-measure all started from scratch simultaneously every 7,980 years.

Counting backward, it seemed that the last time they had all started from scratch was on January 1, 4713 B.C. (They will all be at the starting post again on January 1, 3267 in the Julian Calendar, which will be about March 1, 3267 in the Gregorian Calendar.)

Scaliger therefore suggested that January 1, 4713 B.C. be called Day 1. This suggestion was accepted and this is the system now used in most astronomical calculations. Each day has its number, starting with that far distant one. This number is called the *Julian Day*. Scaliger named it in honor of his father, Julius Scaliger, which means that it has no connection with Caesar, the much more famous Julius. Sometimes, this small posssibility of confusion is avoided by calling it the *Astronomical Day*.

Each such day starts at noon (as is customary in Astronomical Time). Furthermore, this day is not divided into hours, minutes and seconds, but straightforwardly, by the decimal system, into tenths, hundredths, thousandths, and so on. Thus, 3 P.M. on January 15, 1960 will be Julian Day 2,436,949·125.

And so we are back to the day again. Abandoning all frills, astronomers found it best to return to where the whole notion of time starts, to the steady spin of our planet, Earth—the clock we live on.

INDEX

165

INDEX

INDEX

Eclipse, 64, 65, 85, 157
Ecliptic, 84, 103, 104
Egypt, sundials in, 16-17
Egyptian calendar, 125
Egyptian year, 105, 125, 126
Election day, 122
Electric clocks, 56
England, calendar reform in, 134
ephemeris second, 57
equation of time, 36
Equator, 88, 95, 96
  celestial, 100
Equatorial bulge, 159, 160
Equinoctial (Celestial Equator),
  103
equinoctial points, 103
Equinox, 96-98
  precession of the, 159
Era, of Abraham, 147
  Actian, 145
  Augustan, 145
  Buddhist, 160
  Byzantine, 148
  Chinese, 146
  Christian, 149
  Christian Mundane, 148
  chronological, 141
  Common, 150
  Diocletian, 146
  Dionysian, 149
  Fascist, 153
  Greek, 144
  Hindu, 147
  Japanese, 146
  Jewish Mundane, 148
  Julian, 145
  Maccabean, 144
  Macedonian, 144
  Mayan, 146
  Mohammedan, 151
  Mundane, of Alexandria, 148
    of Antioch, 148

  of Armenia, 143, 151
  of Constantinople, 148
  of Nabonnaser, 144
  of the Caesars, 145
  of the Martyrs, 146
  of the Olympiads, 142
  Persian, 152
  Republican, 153
  Roman, 146
  Seleucid, 144
  Spanish, 145
  Syrian, 144
  Syro-Macedonian, 144
  of Varro, 146
Eratosthenes (Greek astronomer),
  104
Eudoxus (Greek astronomer), 126
Eusebius of Caesarea, 147

Fabre d'Eglantine (French poet),
  136
Fall, 75
Fascist Era, 153
February, 77
  days in, 127, 128
First quarter (of moon), 65
Fleming, Sandford, 45
Forenoon, 18, 32
France, time zones in, 47
  weekday names in, 71, 72
Friday, 72
Full moon, 59, 60
  paschal, 119

Galilei, Galileo, 24
Generation, 155
Germany, time zone in, 51
  weekday names in, 72, 73
Gibbous moon, 59, 60
Globe, Celestial, 104
Gnomon, 16
"Good Friday," 72

167

INDEX

INDEX

INDEX

INDEX

INDEX